THE
VILLAGE HOMES
OF ENGLAND

The Village Homes of England

Originally published in 1912 by "The Studio" Ltd. London
This edition published 1995 by Bracken Books, an imprint of
Studio Editions Ltd, Princess House, 50 Eastcastle Street,
London W1N 7AP, England

ISBN 185891 206 7

Printed at Thomson Press (India) Limited

THE VILLAGE HOMES OF ENGLAND

TEXT AND ILLUSTRATIONS
BY SYDNEY R. JONES

EDITED BY CHARLES HOLME

BRACKEN BOOKS
LONDON

CONTENTS.

INTRODUCTION

INTRODUCTION

HE old village homes of England are a precious heritage of the past. Of singular beauty, and fair to look upon, they create a wide and lasting interest. In all parts of the country are to be found many unpretentious examples of quiet and homely taste, erected by the native craftsmen of a sturdy and vigorous peasantry. These buildings are fraught with an appeal to the mind and have a significance deeper than is conveyed by mere terms of stone, of brick, of timber. They stand for much that is peculiarly and characteristically English. They are records of lives well spent ; they tell of contented possession, of love of home, and country, and memory ; they have witnessed the passing of generations of the nation's countrymen, and live on as outward symbols of their intellectual life. With them are associated those ideas of order, of security and comfort, that result from the observance of long-established custom and usage ; they bear witness to well-settled beliefs transmitted from father to son. The old oaks and high elms, the green common fringed by hedgerows, the stile and ancient right-of-way, seem no more the natural growth of time and the soil than do the old rustic dwellings, that bear the marks of antiquity upon them and date back through many ages. It is this sense of settled stability, this association with times far distant from the present, that ever appeal to the imagination and sentiment.

It is not, however, the claims of association that give to these old dwellings their greatest charm ; they possess a more concrete power and arrest attention by reason of their material worth. Considered as examples of building they have much to recommend them, and quietly assert themselves as works of beauty to which time has but given an added value. In them are exhibited the true principles of building, and work showing so much knowledge, so truly observing limitations, so expressive, direct, and honest, must be ranked high in the scale of accomplishment.

The old cottages, as we see them, are the result of a variety of influences and fulfil many conditions which make for good architecture. Ever present there is a feeling for harmony. The harmony that should exist between a building and its surroundings is probably nowhere better illustrated than in the cottages. Set amid natural scenes, in rich valleys, or clustering on the hillsides, they seem part of the landscape ; no conflicting note meets the eye, and building blends with building and with the environment. This characteristic is well demonstrated in the village of Rockingham (page 6), with its cottages of local stone and thatch placed on the ascending hill and overlooking the plain. One reason for this harmony is not far to seek. The builders ordinarily used the materials indigenous to the locality. A stone-producing district shows cottages of stone ; where forests grew timber construction is in evidence ; chalk finds expression in plasterwork ; and the clay lands exhibit the use of bricks.

3

Instances may be multiplied, and throughout the country is everywhere seen this influence of local product.

It must be remembered that England is divided into geological areas which, with the surface growths of timber, account for the variety of building materials. The accompanying map (opposite page) roughly and broadly shows these areas and their yields; many smaller sub-divisions also occur, and the significance of local product can only be properly appreciated by consulting an accurately-made geological map. It can be stated as a fact that the products of nature are best suited to the localities in which they are found; imported materials never so well harmonise with the landscape as those native to it. Red bricks or blue slates look out of sympathy with the stone of a Cotswold village, as do flints among the timbered buildings of Cheshire. The old builders, by using local materials, acknowledged this artistic truth unconsciously doubtless, as economic necessity—governed by high cost of transport—compelled them to use that which was near to hand. To the acceptance of these conditions the excellence of our domestic architecture is largely due. The variety is endless, but the harmony with nature is all-pervading.

Tradition, or ancient custom, considered as an influence on cottage building, has left its evidence in material form. In different districts are to be seen groups of buildings which are all variations of a common type; no two are exactly alike, yet all bear relation one to another; they are the resultant factors of one source of inspiration. It has already been shown how natural product was responsible for local materials; it remained for the craftsmen to fashion them to meet the requirements of the civilisation of their own time. Local needs brought into being certain methods, enthusiasm for work brought certain refinements, and the limited means available fostered restraint. The development of these forces gradually evolved results which well satisfied the prevailing wants. And so traditions became established and were recognised. Different neighbourhoods developed styles of building, very local, and expressive of the life of the native community. Difficulties of communication prevented interchange of ideas, and each district shows its own inherent peculiarities unaffected by outside influences. As generation succeeded generation, local styles were adopted to suit new conditions or fresh methods, but radical changes were unknown. An intense conservatism prevailed, and care was taken not to break down hastily that which had been devised by previous generations and had stood the test of time: in their own works the craftsmen built in faith, not only for themselves, but for the future.

By acknowledging tradition, by treating with respect the memory of former things, the craftsmen did not yield to mere copyism, but added their own stamp, and so gave to their work a living sturdiness and vitality; they gathered together the bequests of their forerunners and clothed them with their own thoughts. Cottages of a district, exhibiting like natural products in construction, agree together in general conception, but the individual and personal note distinguishes habitation from habitation. One village shows work in advance of its neighbour, or the sphere of activity of a particular workman can be traced. The expression of the north

4

Map of ENGLAND shewing the principal Geological Divisions

ROCKINGHAM, NORTHAMPTONSHIRE

6

PRIESTLEIGH, SOMERSETSHIRE

7

NETHER KELLET, LANCASHIRE

country differs from that of the south, as does the east from the west. A Somersetshire dwelling (page 7), as compared with one in Lancashire (above), displays in its features the operation of a different vein of thought. The southern county is one of great natural richness, of wooded uplands and fertile valleys ; the peasantry seem fitted to the genial environment. In manipulation, in play of fancy, the buildings of the locality reflect the nature of the land and the people. Wild, rugged, and strong is the spirit of the northern county, and nowhere does it find better expression than in the old cottages, with their bold, unimaginative details.

Considered as a whole, old cottages throughout England are Gothic in character ; the early ones intensely so, the later ones in a less degree. But this feeling never entirely disappeared. The coming of the Renaissance, the slowly improved facilities of transport and communication, had little effect upon them. Travelling from county to county, it is interesting to see how tenaciously the old traditions were observed and followed. Here and there is seen the introduction of a classic feature, or occasional examples are met with conceived in the classic manner ; but, speaking generally, Gothic in feeling the cottages ever remained. Old workmen, still living, can remember the lingering of the old traditions ; can tell of methods employed, and patterns used, which had their birth in mediæval times. The newer styles spent themselves upon the mansions of the rich, on public buildings, and in the towns, and it was left to builders of small houses and unambitious, homely cottages to keep alive and reproduce the ancient and native practices of the land.

The geological map on page 5 may here be further considered. It forms the key to this volume. The districts now under review are five in number.

8

WILBARSTON, NORTHAMPTONSHIRE

9

The first includes the bordering counties of Somersetshire, Dorsetshire and Wiltshire. Oölitic and liassic limestones are found towards the west, and chalk, with flints, to the east. The buildings are chiefly of stone, or stone, flints, plaster, and brick used in combination; roofs are stone-slated or thatched. Those parts of Berkshire and Buckinghamshire to be considered are situated on the chalk formation; walls of plaster, half-timber, flints, and

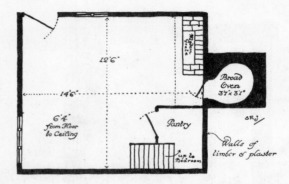

GROUND PLAN OF A COTTAGE AT
LEEK WOOTTON, WARWICK

brick, with roofs of thatch or tile, are common. Oxfordshire, Northamptonshire and Rutlandshire give a beautiful limestone, and the stone buildings of this locality constitute part of the Cotswold group. The chalk formation passes through Hertfordshire, Essex, Cambridgeshire and Suffolk; plaster is the material generally used—either alone or with timber—and roofs are thatched or tiled. Wonderful brick chimneys, and boldly modelled exterior plasterwork, are to be seen here. The northern counties of Yorkshire, Lancashire and north Derbyshire show most conspicuously the use of stone for walls, and roofs of large stone slates.

Cottages stand alone, in clusters, or in rows. The plan was invariably simple and contained within four walls. Its origin in early times and subsequent development, the architectural unit common to all types, and the position of the various features have already been dwelt upon.*
Accommodation varies, from two rooms in the small examples to as many as six or seven rooms in those of more generous dimensions. The cottage of two rooms, when standing alone and small in size, seems to suggest an early type. It has one room on the ground floor, and one above reached by a ladder or stairs opening directly from below. An example exists in which the rooms measure only 10 feet square. The

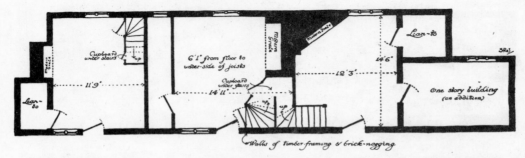

GROUND PLAN OF A ROW OF THREE COTTAGES AT KENILWORTH, WARWICKSHIRE

* "Old English Country Cottages," THE STUDIO, 1906.

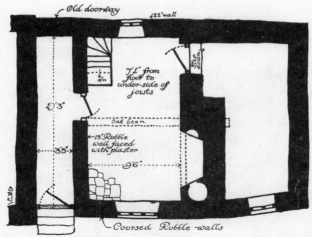

GROUND PLAN OF A COTTAGE AT HANWELL, OXFORDSHIRE

plan from Leek Wootton, in Warwickshire (page 10), shows this arrangement, though the dimensions are larger— 14 feet 6 inches by 12 feet 6 inches. This type of dwelling is now a rarity. More common, but by no means usual, is the cluster or row of cottages, each member having one room on the ground floor and one over, and possibly augmented by outshoots or lean-tos. The three examples from Kenilworth (page 10), now demolished, were disposed in this manner ; at each end a lean-to had been added. Generally speaking, cottages have two rooms on the ground floor and two, sometimes three, bedrooms over. The two stone-built cottages from Hanwell and Great Bourton, in Oxfordshire, shown on this page, have such accommodation.

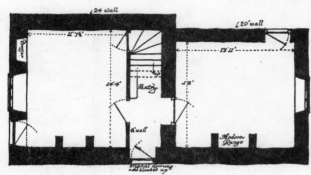

GROUND PLAN OF A COTTAGE AT GREAT BOURTON, OXFORDSHIRE

tion. The Hanwell drawing is interesting, inasmuch as it suggests the

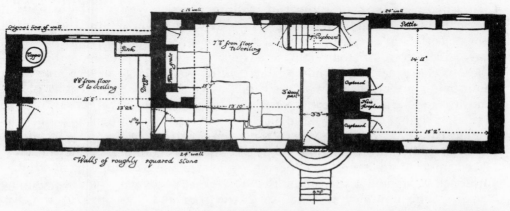

GROUND PLAN OF A COTTAGE AT GREAT BOURTON, OXFORDSHIRE

11

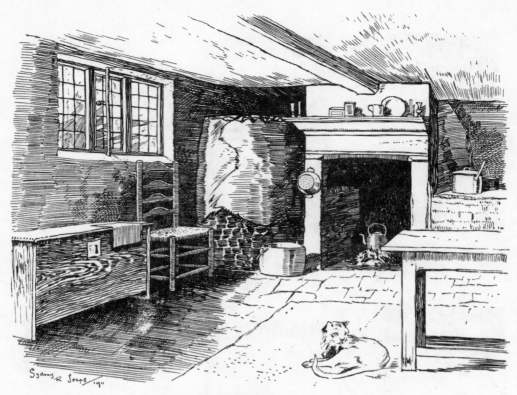

UPPER BODDINGTON, NORTHAMPTONSHIRE

plan of a mediæval hall ; there is the through passage from front to back, and a doorway in it giving access to the chambers of the dwelling. Larger cottages have better convenience, such as is exemplified by the second plan from Great Bourton on page 11.

Frequently there are no foundations, the walls having been erected directly upon the ground. Some walls are of great thickness, particularly when of stone ; on the other hand, those of lath and plaster are often no more than a mere shell. The subject of walling shows a wonderful diversity of material, method and invention. In early times no doubt the ground floor consisted of the bare earth, strewn, for greater comfort, with rushes. Later, floors were of stone slabs, or bricks, or quarries, laid upon the earth. There was a general tendency to keep living-rooms large in size, one good room being preferred to two small ones ; when divided, partitions of oak framing and lath and plaster were used. Fireplaces, where they remain in their original state, are large in size ; their ample dimensions, and the evident careful attention given to their construction, attest to their importance as contributory factors to the cottagers' comfort. The fire was placed upon a stone or brick hearth, as at Upper Boddington, in Northamptonshire (above), or upon the top of low ovens standing on the hearth. The chimney tapered up to the roof and was open to the sky. These open chimneys have now usually been bricked up, and the fire-

LOWER BODDINGTON, NORTHAMPTONSHIRE

13

places filled in and fitted with modern ranges or grates. It must be remembered that households were dependent upon their own resources for supplies of bread, and the common practice of bread-making necessitated provision for baking. The bread oven was at one side of the fireplace, sometimes within the main walls of the building, sometimes projecting beyond; the illustration of Upper Boddington, already mentioned, shows the former arrangement, and the latter method is seen in the plan from Leek Wootton (page 10), and at Mollington, in Oxfordshire, on this page. It was of an oval shape, shallow in height, and domed at the top. A wood fire, placed inside, heated the oven; having served its purpose the fire was removed, the oven cleaned, and the dough put in to bake. The oven door opened into the main chimney and the smoke was thus carried away. With the decline of home bread-making, bread ovens have in a great measure ceased to be useful and are fast disappearing.

The ruined cottage at Lower Boddington, Northamptonshire (page 13), gives a sectional view of the internal construction generally adopted throughout England. The large oaken beam, extending from wall to wall and centrally across the room, carried the joists, which, in turn, supported the floor of the room above. Joists were frequently left exposed on the under side, giving a decorative, timbered ceiling to the room below; or they carried a ceiling of plaster and the main beam only was left to view, often enriched by a simple moulding or chamfer. The height of rooms, from the floor to the under side of the joists, rarely exceeded 7 feet; instances have been noted giving this measurement variously at 5 feet 9 inches, 6 feet 1 inch, and 6 feet 4 inches. All the timber was used in a straightforward, workmanlike

MOLLINGTON, OXFORDSHIRE

14

manner, simply tooled, or left much as it came from the wood-cutter's axe. The illustration shows the purlins and rafters which formed the roof, and the interior walls retaining their old plaster covering apparently composed of lime and sand, with the addition of hair and road scrapings—the composition customarily used by the village plasterer.

Thatch is still a common roof covering, though year by year it becomes less usual, and, for enonomic reasons, is supplanted by tiles or slates. It is invariably picturesque and always harmonizes with the building it covers. The transitory nature of this material precludes the consideration of old work, and it is the survival of old methods and practices that link up past tradition with present usage. At one time it must have been almost universally employed. Thatch requires a roof steeply pitched, so that the wet may be thrown off ; and such roofs, when covered with tiles or slates, are evidences of this earlier form of covering, or of an old style influencing the use of newer materials. The thatcher's art is dying out, and often it is well-nigh impossible to get good thatching done. The older type of men, carrying on the long-practised traditions, seem to have imbibed the past ideals and give great thought to their work. They are careful to see that the straw is first placed in a large rectangular pile and well soaked with water, that it may settle into an almost solid mass upon the roof. The best is then selected, sorted, and tied up into small bundles ready for the thatcher's use. Each bundle has about an even mixture of " heads " and " tails " of straw showing at both ends ; for, being so mixed, they make an even thatch and prevent the hollows forming which are so injurious to its lasting qualities. Reed thatching is distinguished by its great excellence, but reeds are only to be obtained in certain parts of the country.

Viewed in the light of modern knowledge, old cottages have their serious faults. They are often damp, ill-drained, and wanting in convenience and comfort ; questions of site and aspect frequently seem to have escaped consideration. But attention must be given to the fact that sanitary science was in its infancy when they were built ; they conformed to the then prevailing ideas and, presumably, suited the requirements of the people. Conceptions of convenience are comparative attributes and change with each generation ; therefore work exhibiting such meritorious qualities cannot, and must not, be hastily condemned for its now considered faults.

The old country cottage is a relic of the past. Great vernacular styles of building, and the chain of events which produced them, are now but recollections of former things. The ancient picturesqueness and character of our villages are slowly disappearing, and strange it is that such an abandonment of so much that was good has come to pass. But conditions have changed, and present-day life, and thought, and work, make it impossible to build as our forefathers did.

Thoughts of the old inevitably lead to thoughts of the new. To us, in our own time, these survivals of an earlier age have much to teach. A study of them reveals the principles by which good and true work can once more be accomplished, and only by the observance of such principles will a living style in building again arise. It is a moral duty

15

to build our dwellings sincerely and well, to leave a worthy heritage to posterity, and for this end the source of inspiration can only be the good inherited from the past. A desire for houses beautiful to look upon, as well as convenient to live in, the growing appreciation of old work, and the undoubted present revival influenced by it, are happy signs of the times. But these signs are comparatively few and this ugly fact cannot be ignored :—that the average modern cottage or "villa," too painfully obvious to need description, reflects the prevailing spirit of this present age, just as the modest dwellings of an old village bear witness to the ideals of those who built them.

Tradition in art, and excellence in the associated crafts, are vital assets to a nation's welfare : æsthetic influences make life beautiful as surely as material forces make life possible. High standards of taste can only be produced amid sympathetic surroundings, and honest efforts for the common good must be made, fostered, and encouraged. Until that time comes when the new is clothed with vitality and character and beauty, as was the old, until a common encouragement and general appreciation again arises, may the old cottages of England survive and be abiding influences for the good they have in them.

DIVISION I

SOUTHERN PLASTERWORK, FLINTWORK, BRICKWORK AND MASONRY

I.—SOUTHERN PLASTERWORK, FLINTWORK, BRICKWORK AND MASONRY.

A JOURNEY taken directly westward from London leads into the heart of that district anciently known as the kingdom of Wessex. It is a spacious, open country of gently undulating downs, plains, and smooth-outlined hills, and contrasts with the compact richness of Surrey, or the Hampshire water meadows — traversed by little brooks — through which it is approached. The villages nestle cosily in the lower lands and sheltered river valleys. The neighbourhood of Salisbury gives access to the rivers Bourne, Avon, and Wylye; up and down these river banks, overlooked by the uplands—sometimes half-wooded, sometimes treeless—which bound the Salisbury Plain, are to be seen houses and cottages that, collectively, form one of the most distinctive phases of our rural architecture.

The natural product hereabout is chalk; it is revealed by the railway cuttings and old pits from which it has been drawn for generations. Markedly its influence is seen in the walls, plaster-faced and washed a white or ochre colour. Village after village shows such treatment; the low walls, with rough and textural plaster finish, thatched over by roofs with far-projecting eaves. Embowered in trees and, as at the Winterbournes, intersected and bounded by clear streams, these villages present an unending series of pictures, perfect in their way. The buildings are more picturesque than architectural—if these two terms can be dissociated; truly architectural in exhibiting the right use of material and the relation of work to surrounding, yet

STRATFORD-SUB-CASTLE, WILTSHIRE

19

architectural in the homely rather than the grand sense. They have that unconsidered and haphazard look which makes for picturesqueness, but features of more than ordinary interest are absent.

Such cob-walled, plaster-faced cottages as may be seen in the Wiltshire villages differ little in appearance from cottages so contructed in other counties. Upon a low flint base from one to two feet high, the cob-wall was built. It was made of mud, reinforced with flint or rubble or broken bricks. The surfaces, both outside and inside, were finished with a covering of plaster, which was, as already mentioned, washed a white or ochre colour. The heads of the door and window openings were protected by strips of oak. Dormer windows were often carried up from the eaves, and a roof of thatch covered the whole. Extreme simplicity, combined with solidity of construction, was observed in both plans and elevations; the methods employed and materials used were not adaptable to richness or complexity of detail, and the local builders rightly confined themselves to the just limitations of their work.

Flint is found with the chalk, and this material is or predominant interest. It is responsible for a style of building as individually distinctive and local as may be found in England. The work is, in some measure, akin to that of Kent and the Eastern Counties; but while continental influence is largely traceable in the east, the guiding inspiration in Wiltshire was of a purely

SALISBURY, WILTSHIRE

20

MIDDLE WOODFORD, WILTSHIRE

21

WINTERBOURNE EARLS, WILTSHIRE

LOWER WOODFORD, WILTSHIRE

Sydney R. Jones '41

23

WYLYE, WILTSHIRE

English origin. It was the peasant interpretation of a native style which came into being and left its mark alike on mansion, manor-house, and cottage dwelling. The absorbing interest of this flintwork is largely due to the characteristic properties of the material. Flint has a decorative quality peculiar to itself, its colour and its texture making it quite unlike other building materials. Stone differs considerably, some is hard, some soft, and it is warm or cold in colour ; some is to be obtained only in thin layers, while large blocks of another variety are easily procured. But there is always a certain common relationship between the various kinds, and they lend themselves to harmonious effects. And so it is with bricks. But flint is a thing apart, and by its very isolation seems to demand effects of contrast. With this idea in mind the old builders seemed to have worked. A style of building was adopted, the character of which was almost wholly governed by the materials used; flint for the one part, and for the other stone or brick, or both introduced in conjunction.

Flint is difficult to manipulate and requires careful handling. The fine, sharp edges will easily injure the hands, and to-day workmen will, if possible, avoid using it. The varying sizes of broken flints do not easily lend themselves to being laid in even courses. Further, a wall constructed of so many small, irregularly-shaped component parts—as a flint wall is— requires considerable bonding, or binding, to give it stability ; without

24

WINTERBOURNE EARLS, WILTSHIRE

such strengthening it would not hold together. The difficulties imposed by the material were solved by the adoption of a most telling style of work. Instead of bonding the walls with large pieces of flint, as sometimes occurs, it was more usual to use stone or brick for the purpose. In the case of stone a squared block shows alternating with a square panel of flints, draught-board fashion, as may be seen in the example from Salisbury (page 20), and in the gable of the mill at Middle Woodford (page 21). Bricks, used as bonders, generally appear in hori-

zontal courses, breaking through the main walling of flint, and an instance of this is shown in the cottage at Winterbourne Earls (page 22); while at Stratford-sub-Castle (page 19) bricks are set in a haphazard manner, indiscriminately placed. At Lower Woodford (page 23) the two methods are seen introduced into the same wall, a brick string course and an eaves course intersecting the stone and flintwork.

The conscious results of this combination of materials are great in variety and successful in effect. An extraordinary appreciation and realization of surface decoration and texture is manifest. It was produced entirely by a common-sense use of material, acted and re-acted upon by traditional ways and means. Some effects were carried to wonderful lengths —yet always within the limitations of the materials — and the black and white flints, shimmering with glancing light, and set around with the combining bricks or stone, suggest to the mind the brilliancy of a precious jewel.

Flint occurs in irregular nodular masses. It is broken up into small pieces which are dressed to a more or less even size. When freshly broken they are black in colour; some weather slowly, ultimately becoming bleached and white. Between the two extremes, black and white, this

TRENT, DORSETSHIRE

25

material shows an infinite range of greys. Its surface is crystalline—almost glassy—in appearance, and is particularly susceptive to play of light. Broken flints are set in mortar in courses as regular and even as the dressed pieces will allow; or large and small flints are laid without uniformity, an instance of which may be seen at Winterbourne Earls (page 22).

The combination of brick with flint is most in evidence in eastern Wiltshire, near the Hampshire border. Here bricks were easily obtained, and therefore made the economical supplementary material. They framed the doorways and window openings and protected the angles of buildings; at Stratford-sub-Castle (page 19) this arrangement is shown, the window-heads being arched over in the customary manner. Towards the Somerset and Dorset borders, and nearing the stone country, brick gives place to stone. The door-jambs and mullion windows were fashioned of it (page 25), and, as at Wylye (page 24), squared flint and stonework chiefly occur. The gable at Winterbourne Ford (below) partakes of both constructive methods; quoins, window-dressings, and bonding courses are of both stone and brick, intermixed with unconscious dexterity and steadied by the deliberately placed lozenge and two ovals. A rich and effective result accrues.

It is almost impossible, perhaps futile, to ascribe a date to this work. With larger houses the ground is more secure; many offer definite evidence and clearly belong to the Elizabethan and Jacobean periods, and it is reasonable to suppose the earlier cottages were contemporary with them. Later examples bear the obvious signs of work associated with the times of Queen Anne and the Georges, and there is little doubt that a continuous tradition in flint cottage building survived until late in the eighteenth century.

The borderland of Somerset, Dorset, and Wiltshire is productive of stone. Here the chalk formation disappears and with it the plaster-faced and flint-built cottages. An expression of building was developed through, and by reason of, the local stone; and a type of masonry, displaying

26

WINTERBOURNE FORD, WILTSHIRE

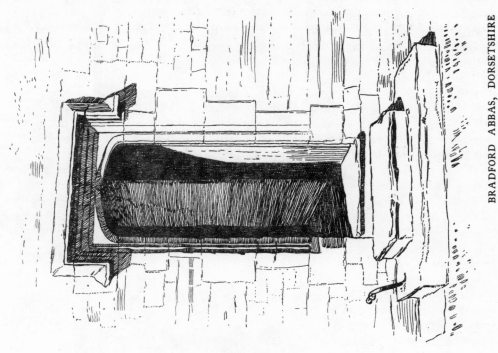

BRADFORD ABBAS, DORSETSHIRE

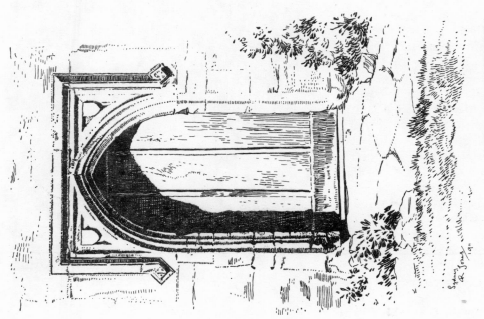

STOFORD, SOMERSETSHIRE

27

great artistic spirit and high manipulative skill, resulted. The mediæval days of monasticism witnessed the erection of noble piles, cathedrals, abbeys, priories, granges. Country churches of the Perpendicular period were of great beauty, marked pre-eminently by their rich and elaborately ornamented towers. The domestic work followed in the wake of the monumental, large houses being equally distinguished though simpler in character, and a corresponding influence is traceable in the smaller dwellings. The freestones of this district are numbered among the finest in England. They are all oölites and come from such famous quarries as Doulton, Bath, and Hamhill. The ease with which the stone can be worked makes it peculiarly suitable for fine and rich effects. It encourages the growth of soft mosses and lichens, and its colour, when mellowed by age, is full of beauty. And so the geological conditions left their impress upon style. The excellence of the available material was largely responsible for the development of a school of masons whose fame spread far beyond the confines of their native locality, and whose skilful handiwork enriched important buildings. Cottage building, necessarily limited in its scope, acquired an importance and distinction which is admirably displayed in the stone-coped gables, ornamented kneelers and finials, arched doorways (page 27), and occasional fine bay-windows. The oölitic formation is bounded on the west by the liassic limestone, and consequently, towards mid-Somerset, walling shows more of the lias and less of the freestone. The strong, gabled projection at Nether Compton, Dorset, shown here, is finished with freestone, but the irregularly coursed walls are of lias. Thatching, as a roof covering, was in many instances displaced by stone. And be it noted that, as the roofing slates were procured in larger sizes than obtain elsewhere, there is a subsequent reduction in the pitch of roofs; the extremely acute angles of,

NETHER COMPTON, DORSETSHIRE

SHERBORNE, DORSETSHIRE

for instance, the Cotswold roots do not occur except where thatch was designed to be the covering.

Few building districts in England seem to have been more imbued with the mediæval spirit than Somerset and its borders. Ecclesiasticism swayed a great influence, and many evidences of its power still exist; place-names and buildings alike bear witness to it. The Gothic feeling, which was the inspiration of the earlier domestic buildings, had its prototype in the churches. And in post-Reformation days this influence continued; slowly, very slowly, it weakened, and early forms and methods continued to live on. In truth, the spirit of the west has always been conservative. John Wood, the architect of Bath, wrote in the eighteenth century, " And it was then only that the lever, the pulley, and the windlass were introduced among the artificers in the upper part of Somerset, before which time the masons made use of no other method to hoist up their heavy stones, than that of dragging them up with small ropes against the sides of a ladder."*

* Bath—British Association, 1888.

29

The early cottage buildings, then, frankly followed the later developments of the Gothic tradition and are marked by its characteristics. The walls were massively constructed and within their thickness window-seats were often introduced, such as is shown in the illustration from Sherborne in Dorset (page 29); the proportions of solids to voids were accurately considered, as were the relations of vertical to horizontal elements; asymmetry and contrast were the formulas relied upon for external effect, and the value of predominant

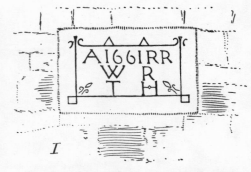

NETHER COMPTON, DORSETSHIRE

roofs and picturesque outlines was realised. Ornaments were kept within proper subjugation, not too rich, yet rich enough to enhance the composition as a whole; the crocketed gable at Nether Compton, Dorset, or the decorated chimney finishing the gable at Trent, Dorset (Nos. 2 and 3 on this page), add just the necessary interest and delicacy. Again, the interesting doorway at Stoford, in Somerset (page 31), arched, and surmounted by a square-headed label, the spandrels being occupied by shields, at once gives character to the whole structure. In passing, it may be noted that the original position of this doorway—that portion to the right hand is a later addition—is reminiscent of the entrance to the "screens" of a more important house. The "screens" was the passage-way, or lobby, formed by the

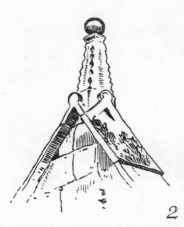

NETHER COMPTON, DORSET-SHIRE

dividing partition which was placed near the end of the domestic hall of the Middle Ages.

Much of the internal arrangement of these earlier buildings is visible on the exterior, emphasised rather than cloaked. The staircase turret at Norton St. Philip, Somerset (page 39), for instance, with its narrow slits for lighting, leaves no doubt as to its purpose; and the positions of fire-places are frequently indicated by wide projecting masonry. Windows were inclined to be small, cusped at the heads, and divided into lights by mullions, as shown in the above-mentioned illustration. At Trent, in Dorsetshire (page 34), the space between

TRENT, DORSETSHIRE

STOFORD, SOMERSETSHIRE

the upper window-heads and label-moulding is decorated by sunk panelling worked in the stone. This same village gives another example of development in window construction, the introduction of the transom (page 36) ; this horizontal feature divides the lights of the four main windows. Bay-windows were employed during the Perpendicular period, though their use was chiefly confined to the larger houses. Two excellent examples may be seen at Norton St. Philip, in Somerset (page 35), boldly jutting out from the main wall, and cleverly finished at the angles with buttresses, obliquely placed. This house is interesting, inasmuch as it exhibits a form of construction uncommon to the neighbourhood ; it will be observed that the upper stories, facing the road, are built of timber and plaster. Whether this work has been added at a subsequent date is by no means plain, and more probably it is an instance of the overlapping of methods. The chimneys, crowning either gable, have the characteristics of the typical Gothic arrangement ; they are short in height and the shafts are pierced with apertures, serving as outlets for the smoke. Another not uncommon form is the slender octagonal shaft, rising from a square base, and terminated with projecting mouldings, as that at Trent (page 36).

Out of the Gothic was developed the customary building style of the countryside which continued on. Examples abound, quiet and restrained in treatment. Priestleigh (page 7) and Aldhampton (page 38) in Somerset, and Corsham, in Wiltshire (page 37), afford instances of the expression

31

CORSHAM, WILTSHIRE

which obtained in Elizabethan days and for many years after. The four-centred, arched doorways of Tudor times, to be seen in the illustrations from Priestleigh and Aldhampton, were adhered to ; square heads displaced the cusping of the mullioned windows, the number of lights was increased, but the label moulding was retained ; gables and dormers were largely used. Materials were applied in an appropriate way, and through all the work this sympathetic treatment is always present. The little stone-tiled hood at Trent (page 25) is as much the legitimate result of available material as is the doorway it protects.

In later days, when the Renaissance was firmly established in England, its influence penetrated into remote places ; the new fashion and the old order developed simultaneously side by side. The range of buildings at Corsham, in Wiltshire (on this page), erected in 1663, evince a more studied and deliberately considered disposition ; part is balanced by part, and the classic inspiration is evident in the details (opposite). The rise of Bath to import-ance during the eighteenth century gave great stimulus to building in the neighbourhood, and many houses were erected, depending upon an Italian ideal for inspiration. But to the towns this influence was chiefly confined, and it is remarkable how little effect the new language of expression in architecture had upon rural cottage building. In the heart of Somerset, and away from the zone of the towns, the village masons, forgetful that the old order changeth, laid stone upon stone, created their patterns, and drew their ideas from the old-time sources, just as did their fathers before them.

CORSHAM, WILTSHIRE

33

TRENT, DORSETSHIRE

34

NORTON ST. PHILIP, SOMERSETSHIRE

35

TRENT, DORSETSHIRE

36

CORSHAM, WILTSHIRE

37

ALDHAMPTON, SOMERSETSHIRE

38

NORTON ST. PHILIP, SOMERSETSHIRE

39

DIVISION II.

BRICKWORK, FLINTWORK, TIMBERWORK AND PLASTER-WORK IN BERKSHIRE AND BUCKINGHAMSHIRE.

II.—BRICKWORK, FLINTWORK, TIMBERWORK AND PLASTER-WORK IN BERKSHIRE AND BUCKINGHAMSHIRE.

ENAISSANCE architecture, tracing its origin to the great revival in intellectual thought that began in Italy during the fifteenth century, was introduced to this country in the early years of the century following. First its influence was little felt ; then a period of transition followed ; and finally it became the dominant marking force of those buildings which were the result of conscious effort and deliberate consideration. But, great as the influence of the Renaissance truly was, it did little, as has already been shown, to materially stem the tide of the inherited building traditions of the countryside. Particularly in the districts producing stone did the old ways prevail—in moorland cottages or hillside villages far away from spheres of active progress. Around London, however, in those parts accessible to, and within the dominion of the metropolis, there is frequently traceable in the cottages a very distinct feeling for the newer development ; it is seen alike in Kent and Surrey, in Berkshire and in Buckinghamshire. Not that the old character was abandoned ; much was retained, but to it was added the local interpretation of the more recent style. Both were contemporaneous, but so well fused and blended together that the resulting compromise often shows much originality and charm.

In cottage building the Renaissance asserted itself chiefly in the details and ornaments. Sash windows appeared, and door and window-heads of jointed bricks were commonly employed. The dormers were not developed upwards from the main walls, but became picturesque and isolated features of the roof. Often roofs were hipped, and beneath the eaves a cornice projected, sometimes consisting of a series of horizontal classic mouldings, sometimes carried out in simple and well-arranged brickwork. Chimneys were rectangular in form and terminated with plain capping, as shown here. The adoption of these

WEST WYCOMBE, BUCK-INGHAMSHIRE

43

DOWNLEY, BUCKINGHAMSHIRE

general forms tended to weaken that strong individuality inherited from the Middle Ages. Work was done more by rote than impulse, and a more or less inevitable common type resulted. But in this work there is revealed again and again evidence of the continual influence of tradition ; especially in the right usage of materials, and the appreciation of their legitimate possibilities, the village builders proved their knowledge, long after the exponents of the fashionable style had forgotten, if they had ever learned, the lesson. The brick chimney at West Wycombe, in Buckinghamshire (page 43), is quite honest in its purpose and construction, and is decorated in a straightforward manner suggested by the material, alternate headers and stretchers projecting from the surfaces of the shaft. In general form it observes the early tradition, wide at the base and standing out from the main wall, giving a sense of strength to the gable end ; but the decoration at the angles, arranged pilaster-wise and arched at the head, betrayed a new motive. The West Wycombe example (page 45), dated 1722, shows the style considerably developed, much more than became usual in general cottage building. The symmetrical disposition of the whole, the projecting cornice, the doorway, centrally placed and surmounted by a winged head, the door-hood, delicately moulded and supported by carved brackets, the plain band of brickwork as a string course, all these features complied with the prevailing taste of the time.

In the southern parts of Berkshire and Buckinghamshire flint, being readily available, largely entered into the construction of the walling. Combined with brick, the materials were thus similar to those used in Wiltshire, but the tendency for horizontal proportions, to be observed in this latter county, is displaced by a feeling for vertical lines. The work is less playful and lacks imaginative treatment. The cottages at Downley,

44

WEST WYCOMBE, BUCKINGHAMSHIRE

45

in Buckinghamshire (page 44), simple and reasonable though they be, have not that power to delight the eye which is the prerogative of the buildings neighbouring the Plain. Indeed, this change of treatment with change of locality is continually appearing in rural architecture, and the effects of local personality and peculiarity are always being seen. Compare the Kentish type of timbered house with that of Cheshire, or the stone dwellings of Dorset with the cottages on the Yorkshire coast. Equivalent materials were used in both instances, oak corresponding with oak and stone with stone. But dissimilar ideas were underlying, which found expression, and affected outward form ; what is severe in one place is fanciful in another ; here is innovation, there conservatism ; or restraint gives way to lively conceits.

Around High Wycombe, in Buckinghamshire, the flints were often arranged in large panels, measuring in some cases as much as nine feet wide. The height of these panels was generally greater than the width and they were bounded on all sides by brickwork, horizontal bands at the bases and heads, and vertical combinations of headers and stretchers at the sides.

Such flint walls that were not divided into panels in this wise were merely protected at the external angles and openings with brickwork, and show no other extraneous material or divisions ; the two examples from Downley (pages 44 and 54) furnish instances and illustrate the particular brick finish given to doors, windows and quoins.

In both Berkshire and Buckinghamshire timber was used in the framing of buildings at a period anterior to, and during the early decades of the Renaissance. The system of construction generally adopted throughout England was followed, and the method has been excellently explained by the late Mr. E. A. Ould in " Old Cottages in Shropshire, Herefordshire and Cheshire." All the distinguishing characteristics are to be seen ; the low wall at the base, more often of stone than of brick, the massive angle-posts and upright timbers, the projecting joists at the first floor level, and the oak pins. At West Wycombe (page 49), the outer ends

WENDOVER, BUCKINGHAMSHIRE

47

UPTON, BUCKINGHAMSHIRE

of the floor joists are covered by a moulded fascia-board; and the delicately-curved brackets, which give support to the overhanging story, are worthy of note. The woodwork of the half-timbered buildings in these two counties is not marked by special singularities or uncommon features. The general good effect, which is always the property of this constructive principle, is present. The work is customary, and no essential difference exists between it and that which may be found in many other districts where timber was easily obtained. The illustration from Sonning, in Berkshire (page 53), shows an example of simple timbering, solid in appearance, and handled in a direct way; while at Wendover, in Buckinghamshire (page 47), the same quiet and satisfying

WEST WYCOMBE, BUCKINGHAMSHIRE

48

WEST WYCOMBE, BUCKINGHAMSHIRE

49

LITTLE WITTENHAM, BERKSHIRE

effect may be seen. The gables and dormers of the former illustration are
continuous from the main wall, and have similar exposed framework ; in
this respect they follow traditional forms. At Wendover, however, the
roof-lines are unbroken at eaves and ridge, and the dormers are appendants
of the roof, clearly denoting a later development. The brick bay with its
corner lighting, shown in detail on .page 46, is a pleasing feature. The
oriel window in the gable at West Wycombe (page 48) is another instance
of picturesque value resulting from workmanlike method.
It is not unusual to find the spaces between the timbers filled with brickwork, called brick-nogging. It occurs in the walls and overhanging gables
at East Hendred, in Berkshire (page 55), and at Dinton, in Buckinghamshire (page 58). In each case the brickwork is arranged herring-bone
fashion, a plan more commonly adopted in the eastern than in the western
counties. But while at East Hendred the timbers crowd closely upon each
other, and the intervening panels are narrow and long, the width of the
panels at Dinton is little less than the height. In timber-framed buildings
it was no doubt originally the custom to fill the interstices with wattle and
dab, and it is evident that, as time went on and bricks became available,
they were often used for the infilling. It has sometimes been questioned
why these two materials should have been used in conjunction, why, with
the advent of bricks, timbers were retained. This combination was greatly

50

EAST HENDRED, BERKSHIRE

51

a result of adhesion to custom.   Timber-building, old-established in practice, was not quickly superseded, and continued long after brickwork became a constituent part of the structures.   Economy, also, was a probable factor ; oak, plentiful and handy, would be cheaper than bricks.   And so, for a period, both were used, side by side.   The discontinuance of half-timber building was due to a number of causes, the chief of which was the growing scarcity of oak in the seventeenth century.   Brick-making at that date had been developed, and was attended by a consequent cheapness of production.   These conditions reacted upon each other ; brick-building, which was not reliant upon a subsidiary material for its development, in a great measure superseded wooden-framed cottage building, which gradually fell into disuse.

The structural frame-work, so boldly exposed on the exterior of half-timbered buildings, had its counterpart within.   The undersides of the floors, with their arrangement of beams and joists resting on the oaken wall-plates, were left visible.   No more decorative ceiling effect, resulting from frank construction, has ever been evolved.   Often the woodwork was merely roughly squared, such as may be seen at Little Wittenham, in Berkshire (page 50).   The main beams were frequently decorated with a simple moulding, or with a stopped chamfer, as at East Hendred (page 51) ; the beam is here supported by a slightly projecting bracket.   This interior shows the usual type of fireplace of the period, wide and deep enough to seat a group within its jambs, and with its accompaniments of an open-hearth, fire-back and chimney-crane, has the constituents of that mental picture—so often dearly treasured but so rarely materially realised—of the old chimney corner.

North of Berkshire, and centrally through Buckinghamshire, runs the chalk formation, continued without break from Wiltshire.   Homely cottages, coated with plaster, abound at Childrey (page 54), and East Hendred (pages 56 and 57),—charming Berkshire villages lying at the foot of the downs which bound the Vale of the White Horse on the south—at Upton, in Buckinghamshire (page 48), and in those old and pretty villages around Aylesbury.   The finish of the cottage walls is generally of ochre colouring, pale or deep in strength, and whitewash is less customary.   Decorated external plasterwork, or pargetting, is not infrequently seen.   The devices take the form of lightly-recessed ornaments, simple in character ; in some cases they extend over the entire surface of the walls, in others they only emphasise special features.   Such a treatment exists at Abingdon, in Berkshire (page 60), where the sunk decoration of the panels, and the narrow bands dividing them, are white, and the remaining work is coloured yellow.   Timber-framed buildings were often plastered over, and the thinness of the superimposed material permits the partial disclosure of the original woodwork.   At Steventon, in Berkshire (page 59), there is an example of this, and the protecting plaster, covering the sunlit cottage at Dinton, in Buckinghamshire (page 58), has done much to preserve the ancient oaken structure.

DINTON, BUCKINGHAMSHIRE

SONNING, BERKSHIRE

53

CHILDREY, BERKSHIRE

DOWNLEY, BUCKINGHAMSHIRE

54

EAST HENDRED, BERKSHIRE

55

EAST HENDRED, BERKSHIRE

56

EAST HENDRED, BERKSHIRE

57

DINTON, BUCKINGHAMSHIRE

58

STEVENTON, BERKSHIRE

59

ABINGDON, BERKSHIRE

STONEWORK IN THE EASTERN COTSWOLDS

III.—STONEWORK IN THE EASTERN COTSWOLDS.

THOSE buildings commonly known as the Cotswold group are not strictly confined to the geographical area from which they take their name. The hills proper, giving the designation, rise steeply from the Severn valley and are mostly confined to the county of Gloucestershire. But stretching far away eastwards, through Oxfordshire, through Northamptonshire, and into Rutlandshire, the face of the country is broken and hilly; it is diversified by high-lying plains and tracts of woodland. From end to end of these low hills extends the broad bed of stone that gives distinction to the buildings lying along its course. In bygone days the oölite and lias was worked from innumerable local quarries, and whether a village community was engaged in the erection of a church, a house, or a barn, it would seek no farther than the nearest quarry for a supply of material.

Architectural styles have often been developed, changed, or abandoned through causes outside and independent of them. The Cotswold building tradition seems to have been so affected. The particular excellence of it was indirectly partly due to England's oldest industry, the production of wool. Sheep-rearing for profit was established shortly after the Norman Conquest, and soon became a flourishing and lucrative occupation. Such success attended the wool trade that English fleeces were sought by foreign merchants and distributed by them through Europe. It ultimately came to pass that the principal supply for the continent was drawn from England. During the reigns of the early Edwards, Flemish artisans settled in this country and under their direction rose the home woollen manufacture. This, in turn, developed as successfully as the unconverted wool trade had done; it attained such dimensions that the exportation of the raw product was prohibited in the reign of Elizabeth. The light soils and hills of the Cotswold country were particularly suited to sheep-farming, and for centuries flocks of great magnitude

GRETTON, NORTHAMPTONSHIRE

63

UPPINGHAM, RUTLAND

grazed on the wolds. Their produce contributed to the national prosperity, and the consequent influx of wealth to the district must have had an important bearing on village life and on the architecture. Splendid churches and houses were erected, and cottages of more than ordinary merit came into being.

The stone yielded is not uniform in character all along the formation. Geologically the same product, the layers of the strata differ greatly in thickness. The building stones procurable are therefore dissimilar in size. The manner of walling in the old work was prescribed by the nature of the near quarry. Masonry was of ashlar—carefully dressed and neatly fitted together,—of coursed rubble, or of random rubble. Often, as at Mollington, in Oxfordshire (page 65), the stones were roughly squared and laid in regular courses of varying depth, the largest being towards the base. This customary practice, of gradually diminishing the sizes of the blocks upward from the ground, was a sound maxim to act upon; for the weighty nature of the lower work imparted a sense of fixed solidity to the foundation, and, contrasting with the smaller upper stones, gave an appearance of lightness and height to the superstructure. Rubble walls—by which is meant walls constructed of rough stones irregular both in shape and size—were protected at the angles with dressed stonework; the cottage at Claydon, in Oxfordshire (page 73), has such freestone quoins. In the county of

64

MOLLINGTON, OXFORDSHIRE

65

SUTTON BASSETT, NORTHAMPTONSHIRE

THORPE-BY-WATER, RUTLAND

66

MORTON PINKNEY, NORTHAMPTONSHIRE

Northamptonshire ironstone is found. Red in colour, it contrasts with the cool and mellow tints of the oölite, and a pleasing surface variety results where the two are seen used in conjunction. Throughout the shire these materials were more or less so employed. Morton Pinkney, in Northamptonshire (page 67), and Lyddington, in Rutland (opposite), furnish instances of ironstone introduced in walling without definite design, isolated pieces or short courses showing dark against the paler surrounding masonry. But ordinarily the builders attempted a deliberate scheme of decoration, obviously considered, and acceding to exact limitation. A system was adopted in which light and red stone ran in alternate horizontal bands. The bands were not even in depth nor necessarily of one course only; two or three courses of the one kind of stone may be found abutting on a single course of the other. Typical illustrations of this parti-coloured Northamptonshire masonry are shown in the two drawings from Wilbarston (pages 9 and 71).

Cotswold villages have a character all their own and are not quite comparable to any other group. The native stone, used within its natural borders, contributes not a little to their captivating beauty. Nestling in the folds of the hills, or, as at Horley (opposite page 64), rising upwards to the higher lands, they delight the eye. Imagination pictures that it was a kindly spirit gave them birth, in spacious times when grace and tranquillity had a place in the daily round. A moral feeling seems to pervade, which gives an impression to the mind not soon forgotten. The charm of these venerable and grey villages is no mere matter of passing moment; their praises, so often sung by distinguished writers, have not been overstated. Many an inspiration for what we now term town or suburb planning may be seen, unconscious arrangements which slowly grew together and adapted themselves to hill and dale. Open spaces and sheltered greens; lanes and by-ways commanding pleasant vistas; simple and harmonious architecture; such

UPPINGHAM, RUTLAND

68

LYDDINGTON, RUTLAND

69

essentials were delicately adjusted one to another in proper relation and with quiet dignity.

The architecture of the Cotswolds is charged with life and individuality, and is distinguished by excellent craftsmanship. It was developed out of the local stone, a material susceptive to many possibilities, and suited alike to all the elements of the buildings. Though some few examples are earlier in date, the established tradition arrived at maturity in the days of Elizabeth; so firmly rooted did it become that it survived in remote parts until comparatively recent times. Not infrequently the work is dated. The occupier's initials and the year—carved in a small panel—appear in a gable, above a doorway, or in some such conspicuous place. Even in these small details certain provincialisms are to be observed. To the westward—that is, in Oxfordshire and on the Northamptonshire border—the lettering and dates are usually contained within a rectangular space framed by simple mouldings (page 72, Nos. 1 and 2); but in Rutland the distinguishing marks are exhibited on a lozenge raised from the face of the stonework as, for example, at Thorpe-by-Water and Lyddington (page 72, Nos. 3 and 5). Judging by the dates carved upon them, the fashion of inserting such panels into cottage walls was not prevalent earlier than the seventeenth century.

The gable is a prominent feature throughout the district. Its use was universal. The pitch is steep and the angle at the apex is more acute than a right angle. Many are protected from the weather by stone coping, and crowned at the head with a finial. The illustration from Claydon (page 73) demonstrates the introduction of kneelers at the two lower corners. At Sutton Bassett, in Northamptonshire (page 66), the gable rises up from the front wall, but it was not unusual to build cottages with their gable-ends to the road, in the manner shown at Lyddington, in Rutland (page 75). Allied to the gable is the dormer, and it almost as frequently exists.

STOWE-NINE-CHURCHES
NORTHAMPTONSHIRE

70

WILBARSTON, NORTHAMPTONSHIRE

Sydney R Jones

71

Literally it is a window in a roof, placed in a small gable of its own. At Gretton, in Northamptonshire (page 63), it so appears, with a dripstone at the head.   A more advanced development is to be seen at Uppingham, in Rutland (page 68).   Here a square bay is carried up above the eaves and finished dormer-wise ; it is capped with a projecting coping, and a sundial ornaments the space above the window.   Again, at Stowe-Nine-Churches, in Northamptonshire (page 70), the polygonal bay shows the dormer treatment ; but whereas at Uppingham the higher window is partly in the roof, the window in this instance stops at the roof level.   The way in which the corbels have been introduced above the side lights should be noticed, and how thereby the face of the gablet has been brought into one plane.

Windows were flat at the head and, when constructed of stone, were divided into lights by mullions.   The label, which was placed over them, is shown in many of the drawings.   It may be square-headed, following the form of the window, or it may appear as a single horizontal moulding, simple in section and not returned at the extremities.   Fine bay-windows greatly enhanced many successful effects of grouping.   They were used with discrimination, and carefully disposed ; wall-spaces were nicely broken by their projection, and distinction added to the complete composition.   At Uppingham, in Rutland (page 64), two bay-windows are seen symmetrically placed at each side of the doorway.   But this balanced order was uncommon, and it was usual to add bay-windows singly, as at Uppingham and Stowe-Nine-Churches mentioned above.   Occasionally they project in rectangular form from the front of the building, in the way shown at Mollington, in Oxfordshire (page 82) ; generally, however, they come obliquely outwards.   The Caldecott bay (page 76), with the face of its upper compartment gradually increasing in width, is of the local type that subsists in the neighbourhood of Rutland.   A semicircular, or bow-window, is illustrated from Lower Boddington, in Northamptonshire (page 74). Built of wood upon a low stone base, it is obviously later in date than the foregoing ; in fact this feature is primarily associated with the eighteenth century.

The four-centred depressed arch of Tudor times, surrounded by a rectangular moulded frame, survived in many stone cottage

DATE PANELS

72

CLAYDON, OXFORDSHIRE

73

doorways. Those at Caldecott, in Rutland (page 77), and at Great Bourton, in Oxfordshire (pages 78 and 79), are representations of the olden method. In both the latter examples the original oak door has been retained; each is divided into panels by applied fillets, and studded with large nail-heads. The labels of the doorways harmonise with those of the windows, and are sometimes emphasised by a more lavish treatment. At Great Bourton (page 78), the horizontal returns are beautifully decorated at their termination. Doorways, indeed, were given importance and were regarded as worthy objects upon which to bestow the best craftsmanship. The dressed stone chimney on the gable end at Thorpe-by-Water, in Rutland (page 66), delicately adorned with classic mouldings, is of a type which, with variations, was adopted throughout the Cotswolds. Such general forms of detail were accepted, and continually recur. Individuality played upon a sure and firmly-rooted background, evolved by time and practice. There was concord in the choice and allocation of parts, an understanding of possibility, of harmonious relationship. Thus it is revealed how a great tradition was built up that deservedly takes rank as a masterpiece of English style.

New methods can be detected in some of the later buildings, faintly reflecting the classic influence that became the guiding fashion of stately architectural design. Mostly in the details the changes are seen, as in the dormer at Ashley, Northamptonshire (page 80), which is a distinct feature of the roof. The house at the end of the bridge, shown in the coloured drawing from Geddington, in Northamptonshire (opposite), in its dormers and wooden-framed windows heralds the change of style, while over the doorway appear a fanlight and projecting hood. At Upper Boddington, in the same county, is a complete little specimen of work moulded in the newer way (page 81); it is a homely rendering, sober in effect and not without a certain dignity. The arrangement, as a whole, has a considered aspect, and contrasts with the lively charm and playfulness of the earlier tradition. Sash windows have displaced the mullioned form, the quoins are raised, the mouldings have a classic profile. But the windows are not evenly disposed, and there is a licence of treatment shown in many minor directions. The old feeling had not disappeared; it lived on clothed in fresher garb, owning freedom and not exactness.

LOWER BODDINGTON
NORTHAMPTONSHIRE

74

LYDDINGTON, RUTLAND

75

CALDECOTT, RUTLAND

76

CALDECOTT, RUTLAND

77

GREAT BOURTON, OXFORDSHIRE

78

GREAT BOURTON, OXFORDSHIRE

79

ASHLEY, NORTHAMPTONSHIRE

80

UPPER BODDINGTON, NORTHAMPTONSHIRE

81

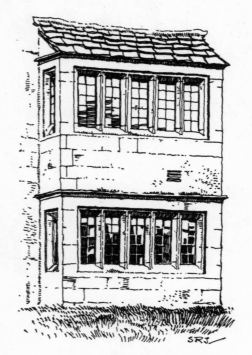

MOLLINGTON, OXFORDSHIRE

DIVISION IV

PARGETTING, TIMBERWORK, BRICKWORK AND THATCHING IN THE EASTERN COUNTIES

IV.—PARGETTING, TIMBERWORK, BRICKWORK AND THATCHING IN THE EASTERN COUNTIES.

PLASTERING, as an art, was largely practised in the eastern counties of England. In its early form—known by the name of "wattle and dab"—plasterwork was used for the filling in of panels formed by the vertical and horizontal timbers of wooden-framed structures. It was made of interwoven hazel-rods and clay, and covered, both internally and externally, with a mixture of lime and sand. Such was the primitive method, and out of it grew the native school of plasterwork. The craft had attained considerable prominence by the end of the fifteenth century; it received great stimulus when Henry VIII. engaged Italian workmen who revealed the decorative possibilities of plaster.

Onward from that time plasterwork became the fashion. It was the principal feature of many buildings, confined not only to interior decoration but employed as ornamental treatment on the exterior. Reaching a full development in the seventeenth century, external plasterwork survived in out-of-the-way places well into the eighteenth.

How far the style of village work was affected by foreign influence—Italian or otherwise—it is difficult to estimate. It was of native growth, and if outside forces were assimilated, they merely brought a new development to that which had persisted for generations. The country plasterer would be slow to change, diffident to forsake the ways he had inherited. This desire on the part of

SUDBURY, SUFFOLK

85

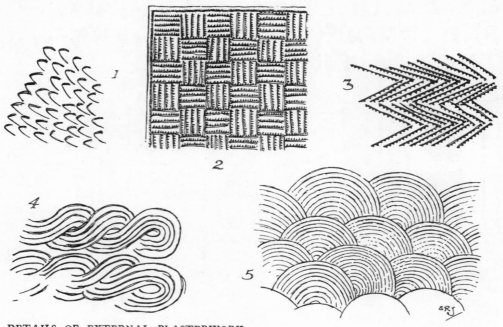

DETAILS OF EXTERNAL PLASTERWORK

the worker to cling to accepted methods, his opposition to innovation, and his slowness to adopt new forms, runs through all old traditions of humble building effort, and must not be overlooked when the consideration or judgment of such work is the object. In this it differed from those efforts of greater pretension which were based on the deliberate styles of trained architectural schools, always susceptible to the ebb and flow of changing fashion. Particularly in plasterwork is demonstrated how permanent and fixed local practice may become. Certain peculiarities are often confined to very small areas, they occur again and again within circumscribed limits ; but beyond the confines of the little districts they are displaced by other distinguishing marks. It is evident that old patterns were perfected and used in the region of their origin, and were transmitted from father to son. Although plaster is not the exclusive building product of the eastern counties, it is there most in evidence. The country is generally level, relieved here and there by easy prominences. Big rolling skies sweep over low landscapes, divided by bright patches of pasture or fine corn-lands. Very fitting are the little white villages, with red-tiled or thatched roofs, and sheltered by high trees. Such is Great Bartlow, in Cambridgeshire (opposite), typical of many villages that abound. The material used for the covering of cottage walls came to be known by the name of " parge," and the art of applying it was called " pargetting." The units of the composition are stated by Mr. George Bankart* to have been " ordinary lime and sand and hair. This material, which was similar to that now used for the parging of flues, contained a certain amount of cow-dung and road

* " The Art of the Plasterer," George Bankart.

86

GREAT BARTLOW, CAMBRIDGESHIRE

87

DETAILS OF EXTERNAL PLASTERWORK

scrapings, and became, as time went on, the decorative medium of the *native English Playsterer.*" Chopped hay was sometimes substituted for hair, while a ruined cottage at Melbourn, Cambridgeshire, showed that straw had been added to the mixture.

Parge, simple and economic material though it was, gave scope for effective display. Its possibilities were appreciated and work full of variety ensued. Local plasterers plied their craft, knowing and using their material as old workmen were wont to do : fashioned it deftly, and applied their home-bred stamps and patterns in a sane, direct way. Especially applicable was pargetting to the cottage walls. Some were plain and unembellished, some rough-cast ; while others were " pricked," panelled, recessed, or modelled in relief. Of simple plaster cottages, such as that at Melbourn (page 106), there are yet remaining a great number. It was not unusual to cover timber-framed houses with plaster in the manner shown at Stoke-by-Nayland (page 105), and Stoke-by-Clare, in Suffolk (page 103). The main structural timbers would generally be disclosed. Interesting is the angle-post of the former illustration, and the series of wooden shafts, crowned by Gothic caps from which spring the brackets that support the

CLARE, SUFFOLK

DETAILS OF EXTERNAL PLASTERWORK

oversailing story. The barge-board of the latter example has the guilloche pattern of Elizabethan and Jacobean times carved upon it. At Therfield, in Hertfordshire (page 99), the plastered cottage front of timber construction is partly covered by weather-boarding, a system more peculiar to the south than to the north of London.

Patterns in plaster show a number of forms and arrangements. The ground was laid with nice discrimination, varied in its surface and texture, and was not of the uniform, true dead level by which plastering is now characterised. Upon the moist ground tools were worked in an endless number of ways. Their application imparted diapered effects, unobtrusive in themselves, yet adding interest. Common are the pricked incisions—apparently done with a pointed stick—which often repeat over the entire wall space (page 86, No. 1). The "herring-bone" (page 86, No. 3) is another pattern that was much employed, evidently produced by an implement having one edge running in zigzag lines, as the illustration shows. This same tool appears responsible for the interchanging squares (page 86, No. 2) made by combining short vertical and horizontal lines. Flowing patterns (page 86, No. 4), scalloped fans (page 86, No. 5), and many other devices found a place in the medium of pargetting.

It not infrequently happens that the surfaces are divided into rectangular panels. Each panel will be bounded by a scratched moulding, low in relief and of simple section. Maybe the panels are diapered or pricked, in contrast to the plain dividing spaces, as at Little Hadham, in Hertfordshire (page 94) ; or both panels and surrounding frames will be devoid of relief. At Ashwell, in Hertfordshire (page 88, No. 3), the moulding is similar to bead enrichment, and the triangular panel, bearing the date,

90

CLARE, SUFFOLK

91

has the repeating square pattern. A certain number of buildings depend upon recessed designs for their added decoration, obtained in most instances by the application of wooden templates. In this wise were made the ornaments and borders on the cottages at Clare, in Suffolk (page 89) ; and a reference to the details numbered 1 and 2 on page 88 will show the shape of the sunk patterns which were formed by surrounding the templates with rough-cast.

Exterior ornamental modelling furnished a field for the expression of such flights of fancy as the East Anglian plasterer chose to indulge in. Here was room for free action. If his work was sometimes too ambitious, sometimes lacking in knowledge and refinement, it was spirited and always logically developed out of the material. The less elaborate specimens are the best ; delicate running patterns, scroll work, or foliated representations inspired by the pleasant, natural surroundings in which the village worker spent his days. Many of these are excellent in every way, and betray skill and accomplishment on the part of the executant. Such is the decoration on the front of the example from Clare, in Suffolk (page 91).

It stands out in considerable relief, and the details on page 90 show how vigorously it was handled ; the panels are divided by ovolo mouldings. At Ashwell, in Hertfordshire, is a cottage front dated 1681 (opposite), panelled, and ornamented with scroll designs and a rude presentment of a dolphin, or some kindred monster (page 88, No. 4). The parge decoration at Saffron Walden, Essex (page 95), is on a large scale, and figures that exceed life-size enter into the scheme. The work belongs to the seventeenth century. There is much interesting modelling on the gables, as the drawings on page 97 demonstrate. The themes were mostly of natural origin, birds, fruit and flowers; while quoins and dividing bands were formed with templates and slightly project, as does the series of crossed arches beneath the window. To a late date in the development of plastering must be assigned the example from Little Chesterford, in Essex, appearing on this page. Classic feeling is evident, both in the disposition of the parts, and in the forms

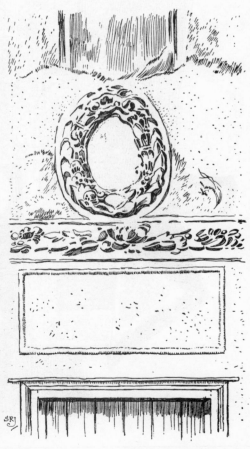

DETAILS OF EXTERNAL PLASTERWORK

92

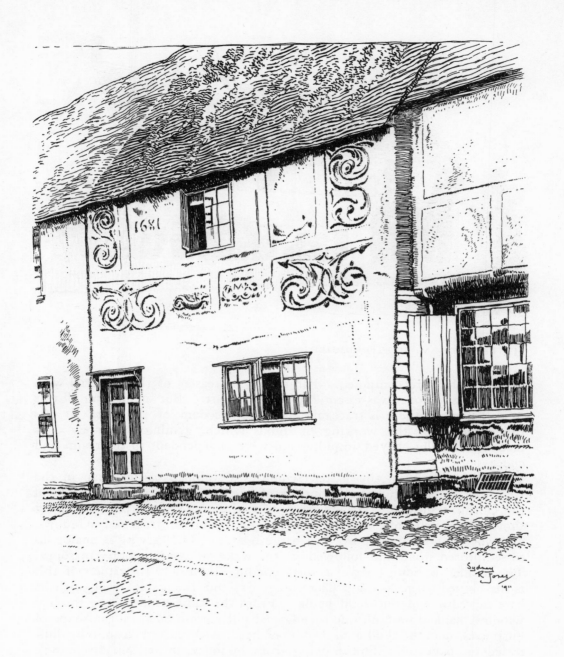

ASHWELL, HERTFORDSHIRE

93

LITTLE HADHAM, HERTFORDSHIRE

of which they are composed. Pargetting, by reason of the material with which it was done, was essentially a homely art. But underlying all this modelled work there is traceable a certain freedom of thought. It was the outcome of the working of minds which, gaining power by contact, individually obeyed impulse, and were independent in their aim and endeavour.

Timber building in the eastern counties developed earlier than in the west. It is often rich and beautiful, of fine execution, and in the style of the Gothic tradition. Woodwork outside the range of the present subject shows how delicately wrought were the elaborate traceried windows, doorways, carved angle-posts, and barge-boards. The carving is analogous to sculptured stone and followed in the wake of contemporary masonry. The smaller buildings have a corresponding interest. In witness of this is the cusped barge-board at Clare (page 91) and the gable oriel, with its base carved out of one solid baulk. From the same example are the bay window, flanked on each side by engaged pillars, fashioned in the shape of buttresses, and the Tudor arched door-head, with carved spandrels, illustrated on page 96. The drawing from Sudbury, in Suffolk (page 85), shows a characteristic oak-framed window, while over the door is an enriched lintel. The window is divided into lights by mullions and has a horizontal crossbar, or transome. Throughout this district, where once great forests grew, are innumerable specimens of half-timbered cottages, built in the traditional manner that prospered in the countryside. Of these, Little Chesterford, in Essex (page 101), furnishes an instance ; it is solid in appearance, honest in construction, and picturesque to look upon. A group at Stoke-by-Nayland, in Suffolk (page 104), is effectively broken up

SAFFRON WALDEN, ESSEX (SEE PAGE 97)

95

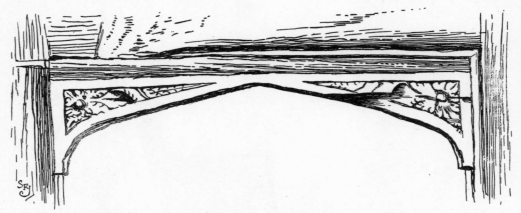

CLARE, SUFFOLK

by irregularly placed gables, and dominated by a fine
chimney-stack with clustered shafts. The upright
timbers are set close together, and the framework
is strengthened by diagonal braces.

Stone is not a common product of the eastern
counties. It occurs in parts—for instance, in Cambridgeshire, which produces a hardened form of
chalk called "clunch"—but generally over this area
building stones are scarce. The absence of stone
and the presence of good brick-earths brought about
the development of brickwork. Many of the earliest
English examples—other than those of Roman origin
—are to be found in Norfolk, Suffolk, and Essex.
It was, however, in the erection of castles, old halls,
and manor houses that this material was used, and
no permanent brick building tradition for cottage
work seems to have existed in early times. But
after chimneys had become by custom and necessity
established adjuncts to all types of dwelling—that is
to say, in the sixteenth century—they were the
special features of the cottages to which brickwork
was almost invariably applied. They were treated
as important items of the architectural groups, not
suppressed, but emphasised. Upon them craftsmen
lavished their best skill. Many noble shafts bear
witness to their handiwork and power of design.
Often several flues were grouped together in one
great stack, while above the roof the single shafts
appeared in clusters. Such chimneys may be seen
in the drawings of Stoke-by-Nayland (page 105)
and Melbourn (page 106), already mentioned. The
shafts were shaped in various ways, rectangular,
octagonal, circular; each might be entirely detached,

CLARE, SUFFOLK

96

DETAILS OF EXTERNAL PLASTERWORK (SEE PAGE 95)

97

ASHEN, ESSEX

or partially so and connected by moulded bases and caps ; some were all joined together without break. The examples from Newport, in Essex (page 102), are richly diapered with small face patterns, different on each shaft. The chimneys at Newton Green, in Suffolk (page 101), distinctly suggest the Continental influence which exercised a sway all along the eastern coast. The actual bricks then used were beautiful in themselves. Clay was weathered by long exposure, and the process of making by hand conduced to a pleasing variety in shape. They were burned in the old-fashioned way and were uneven in texture and colour. The proportions were good ; old bricks were thin and rarely, if ever, exceeded two inches in depth. Mortar joints were flush with the face of the brickwork and were not often less than half-an-inch in width. The mortar was generally, though not always, light in colour and of excellent quality : so good, in fact, that it is often only with difficulty that old brickwork can be parted. Old chimneys, it is said, have been bodily moved from one place and re-erected in another, so firmly were they jointed together.

Roofs were occasionally made up with tiles of two or more colours, laid in shapes and patterns, or in parallel bands, as at Clare (page 89). The contrasts are never very decided and the colours always blend. But the thatched roofs are the glory of the district. Although there is in many parts of England no great difference existing between thatching, none can compare with that of the eastern counties. There it reached a state of perfection beyond which it is difficult to imagine. Thatching was an art, full of life

98

THERFIELD, HERTFORDSHIRE

99

TRUMPINGTON, CAMBRIDGESHIRE

and invention; the work was skilful and sure. All sorts or arrangements of hazel rods were interwoven and crossed. The thatch was cut back in patterns, elaborated at the ridges, and projected at the points of gables. The details from Cambridgeshire shown on this page are characteristic. Deep covered dormers, exemplified by the drawings of Trumpington, Cambridge- shire (above), and Ashen, Essex (page 98), are prevalent and always pleasing to the eye. There is, indeed, a quality possessed by thatch peculiar to itself. It has colour and beauty, and nothing more harmonious, more satisfying in effect, has ever formed the roofs of England's village dwellings.

DETAILS OF THATCHING FROM CAMBRIDGESHIRE

NEWTON GREEN, SUFFOLK

LITTLE CHESTERFORD, ESSEX

101

NEWPORT, ESSEX

102

103

STOKE-BY-NAYLAND, SUFFOLK

104

STOKE-BY-NAYLAND, SUFFOLK

Sydney
R
Jones/1911

MELBOURN, CAMBRIDGESHIRE

106

DIVISION V

NORTHERN MASONRY AND BRICKWORK

V.—NORTHERN MASONRY AND BRICKWORK

VILLAGE craft-work in the North of England possesses distinctive characteristics, and its peculiarities are well defined. The buildings bear a relationship to those elsewhere, yet are a type in themselves, divided from the main trend of architectural development by their own particular features. Nowhere is the effect of local influence more apparent. They betray the individuality, the outlook upon life, and the conception of things, that distinguished the northern from the southern mind. Work in the north and south, considered together, is in a small degree comparable to the architecture of different peoples, which displays manifest contrasts of race and creed. It was no trifling spirit that brought into being the cottages on the Yorkshire wilds, or those in the mountainous district of Lancashire. Here nature was in stern mood, the elements had to be resisted. There is a certain rugged character in the buildings, accurately representing the external circumstances and underlying powers that were continuous and permanent.

Of all the influences that operated to determine the appearance of these stone-built cottages, that of temperament seems to have been the most potent. The species of stone procurable, it is true, was of much significance. Mr. Alfred Gotch says that "in Derbyshire, Yorkshire, and Lancashire, where the stone is hard, the work is of a plainer and more severe type"* That well sums up the general run of cottage work, a

FIRWOOD FOLD, LANCASHIRE

* "The Growth of the English House," J. Alfred Gotch.

APPLETREE, LANCASHIRE

consequence of the use of material. But it was not always so. In the districts of the oölite—similar to that found in the Cotswolds and Somersetshire,—or where the magnesian limestone occurs—such as was used in building of King's College Chapel, Cambridge,—the same severity is seen, although the stone was suited to the richest effects of workmanship. This leads to the supposition that the great working factor was the temperament of the northerner, his interpretation was quite personal. He used his material in his own way, and his efforts bore evidence of his nature.

The rough northern climate played its part in determining the type or architecture, and accounted in no small way for that austerity by which it is distinguished. The cottages bear testimony to this, and nothing more suggestive of climatic conditions can well be imagined. There, perched on high and exposed places, as at Appletree, in Lancashire (above), or Clapdale, in Yorkshire (page 111), they seem to defy wind and storm. They are, too, admirably suited to their surroundings. One has only to travel over the mountains and moors of Lancashire, Yorkshire, and Derbyshire, to see and feel how well the way of building was adapted to local conditions. The mountains are grand and solitary ; while below, the wild loveliness of romantic dales, watered by fast-flowing rivers and streams, is ever alluring. The stone crops out from the mountain sides in huge, craggy masses, and the buildings, of like material, form an integral part of the landscape. There is such agreement in the whole, such harmony, and the eminent merit of the northern villages lies in this fact. It is their appropriateness that gives them their claim to serious consideration as architecture, and the drawings of Knaresborough, in Yorkshire (page 113), and Stanton-in-the-Peak, in Derbyshire (page 115), demonstrate this point.

Oölite, lias, magnesian limestone, sandstone, and carboniferous limestone, are all found in the three counties. Much of the stone is of a dull and sombre colour, enlivened here and there by patches of warmer hue, as is shown in the coloured drawing from Penistone, in Yorkshire (opposite).

Sydney R Jones

BASLOW, DERBYSHIRE

Some was well dressed and used in large sizes ; such ashlar work has very
fine joints of mortar.   Other large stones were only roughly dressed, with
the joints wide and finished flush with the walls.   Where small building
stones were employed, the quoins would invariably be of large, squared
stones.   Bonders often project considerably beyond the face of the walls.
The hardness of most of the stone, and the massive sizes in which it was
procured, account for a number of the peculiar features of northern work.
Foremost there are the roofs.   Huge flagstones went to their making,
whose weight necessitated a very low pitch.   At Halton, in Lancashire, a
lean-to roof was noticed, covered by two stone slates only, of enormous
size ; and it is by no means uncommon to see roofs having in depth no
more than six courses of slates.   Several of the illustrations show these
stone roofs, Appletree (page 110), and Knaresborough (opposite), and
Stanton-in-the-Peak (page 115), already mentioned.   In these instances
the slates gradually diminish in size towards the ridge.   As soon as another
method of roof-covering was adopted the rake was altered ; to cite an
example, it was made more acute at Baslow, in Derbyshire (above), to
accommodate thatching.   The nature of the stone determined the type of
doorways and windows.   Window openings were made with four stones,
one for the lintel, another for the sill, and an upright piece on each side.
Heads of doorways were formed with one large stone, which boldly crowned
the opening.   The cottages at Eyam, in Derbyshire (page 117)—tragically
known by association as the " Plague " cottages—have this arrangement of
masonry for doors and windows.   It was, and still is in some districts, the

112

KNARESBOROUGH, YORKSHIRE

113

custom to whitewash the exterior face of stonework, in the manner of the far buildings at
Dent, in Yorkshire (page 119). Doorways and
windows would then be accentuated by colouring
the masonry which surrounded them.

The refinement and fanciful treatment so common
to stonework in the southern counties is absent
here. What ornament there is has little in it to
arrest the eye. Details—gable finials, kneelers,
and the like—often border on crudeness. Of
an elementary character are the two chimneys
from Halton, in Lancashire, and that from Burton
Leonard, in Yorkshire, all of which are illustrated

HALTON, LANCASHIRE

on this page; yet they are perfectly suited to the buildings they serve.
The same feeling is evident in the date panel from Scotton, in Yorkshire
(page 122, No. 2), with its quaint attempt at carving in low relief. The
lights of stone windows are narrow, divided by heavy mullions, and have

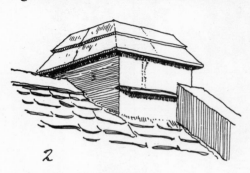

2

HALTON, LANCASHIRE

over them a protecting label, as at Firwood Fold, in Lancashire (page 109).
Many stone-framed windows have
glazing contained in wooden lights,
and these lights are neither casement
nor sash, but slide to and fro; the
windows at Eyam (page 117) open
in this way. The employment of
wooden eaves-gutters, down-spouts,
and rain-water heads was general,
and examples are shown from Green
Hammerton, in Yorkshire, and Halton,
in Lancashire (page 116, Nos. 1 and 2).

Down-spouts are square in section and consist of four pieces of wood, nailed
together. Some gutters are moulded on their outer face, as is the one at
Green Hammerton, just mentioned. Villagers throughout the north of
England make a practice of sanding the steps to doorways. It is an odd

custom, many years old, which still survives. The stone step is run over with
water, partly dried, and to the damp
surface is applied dry sand or sandstone.
Varied are the patterns that are worked
on risers and treads. One from Dolphin-
holme, in Lancashire, is given on page
116; it is carried out in white and ochre-
coloured sand, upon cool, grey stone.

In the neighbourhood of Lancaster is to
be found a type of doorway of quite a
special kind, which does not, to the present writer's knowledge, occur elsewhere.
It is distinguished by the particular

3

BURTON LEONARD, YORKSHIRE

114

STANTON-IN-THE-PEAK, DERBYSHIRE

115

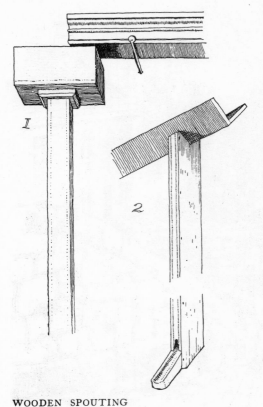

WOODEN SPOUTING

enrichment of the headstone. Over the doorway are two sunk panels, surrounded by a moulding which is continued upwards from the jambs, and the raised centre panel commonly carries a carved date and initials. These dates denote the period at which this fashion in doorways was prevalent; those at Halton, in Lancashire, and at Lancaster (page 121) are dated 1672 and 1701 respectively; and the restored cottage at Abbeystead (page 123) has an old lintel dated 1677. Simpler ornamental doorheads are illustrated from Wyersdale, Lancashire, and Lancaster (page 122, Nos. 1 and 3).

By their form and treatment, and by their repetition at different periods, the ornaments and details show how carefully old tradition was maintained and how tardily it was abandoned. The old villagers were loyal to the naturally developed style. Conservatism was fostered by the nature of the country and its isolation; its influence is obvious in the buildings of the northern counties. Over a very long space of time variations of the same forms were employed, and work belonging to the eighteenth century, especially in the higher parts of Yorkshire and Lancashire, differs little from that of 150 years earlier. Of comparatively recent work Professor Blomfield states that "even in the mill architecture of the Yorkshire manufacturing towns, harsh and forbidding as it is, there remained a certain local quality, and some of the dignity of the eighteenth century in buildings erected as late as 1840."* When a change from the old tradition did come, and the conquering classic influence was drawn upon for inspiration, the new manner was but imperfectly understood, and a clumsy, heavy interpretation, lacking in delicacy, was generally the

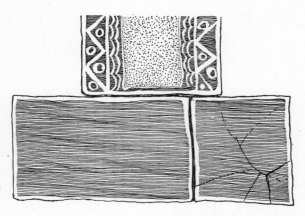

SANDED ENTRANCE STEPS

* "Renaissance Architecture in England," by Reginald Blomfield, M.A.

EYAM, DERBYSHIRE

117

STAVELEY, YORKSHIRE

result. Strangely incongruous some of these small buildings, which show the change in fashion, look ; and, however suited such types may be to certain kinds of landscape, they seem misplaced among the rugged, mountainous scenery of the Pennines.

A remarkable interior exists at Staveley, in Yorkshire, and is illustrated on this page. It is primitive in its arrangement, and gives a good idea of what, apparently, was once the customary abode of the village worker and his family. Two rooms are on the ground floor and there is no upper story. The stone walls are inwardly faced with plaster. There is no ceiling, the timbers of the roof being thus exposed to view. At one end of the cottage a small upper floor has been inserted, extending from the cross-beam to the gable-end. This was the sleeping apartment. It is shown by the diagram on this page and was reached from below by a ladder. The two triangular spaces framed by the beam, posts, and rafters

ENTRANCE TO SLEEPING LOFT OF ABOVE COTTAGE

118

DENT, YORKSHIRE

119

FARNHAM, YORKSHIRE

of the roof, are boarded over, and the central open space was the place of access.
By people of the twentieth century such a place for sleeping may well be
considered rudimentary, and there is small wonder that this habitation has
now been condemned by the local authorities. The stone fireplace from
Farnham, in Yorkshire (above), is not without interest, and is another
instance of the continuance of olden practice. It has much in common
with fireplaces of the thirteenth century, and resembles them in the shallow
depth of the hearth, and in the heavy stonework at the head supported by
corbels.

On the flat lands around York are cottages with walls of brickwork and
pantile roofs. The bricks are pale in tint and lack colour. Front walls
are generally wholly of brick; some show alternate horizontal divisions of
brick and rubble, while many back and interior walls are of the two
materials, or of stone only. Simple string-courses were employed to ornament and break up surfaces of plain walling; they consist of ordinary
or moulded bricks, manipulated in a satisfactory way, and show as dentils,
projecting courses, or bricks laid dog-tooth fashion at an angle to the wall's
face. Under the eaves, and at the first floor level of the cottages at Green
Hammerton, in Yorkshire (page 124), the brick string-courses may be seen.

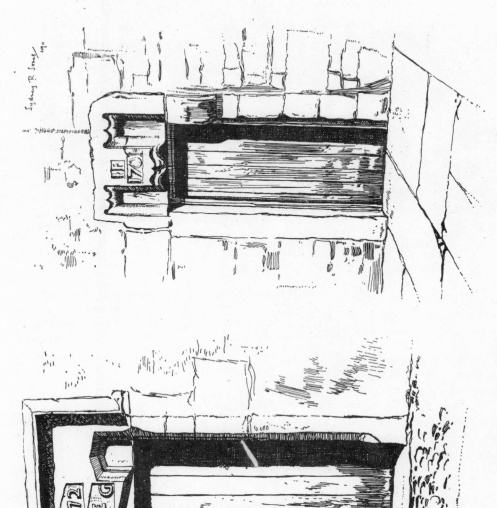

LANCASTER

HALTON, LANCASHIRE

121

FARNHAM, YORKSHIRE

The gable-end of this example is of a kind that can often be observed in the district round; in fact, such gables are prevalent throughout the north-eastern counties, and are as much features of Suffolk as of Yorkshire. They are singular in having an angular arrangement of brickwork opposing the horizontal courses, and flush brick copings at the head. The use of pantiles for roofs was very general and they found their way into the stone regions, as the illustration from Farnham, in Yorkshire (above), demonstrates.

Half-timbering, although it was a building method of the towns and found favour with erectors of large halls, is not conspicuous in the country villages. At York (page 125), Bolton, and elsewhere examples are to be found, while the timbered halls of southern Lancashire are justly famous. But it is not in the timberwork, or in the brickwork, that the real architectural expression of the northerner is to be sought. In the stonework this lies; in the scattered dwellings of Derbyshire, Yorkshire, and Lancashire.

DATE PANELS

122

ABBEYSTEAD, LANCASHIRE

123

GREEN HAMMERTON, YORKSHIRE

YORK

125

DIVISION VI

METALWORK AND WOODWORK

VI.—METALWORK AND WOOD-WORK.

THE direct and straightforward methods that characterised the handling of the building materials for the village dwellings were applied to the making of their metal fittings, and to those movable objects which added to the convenience of daily life. Primarily utilitarian, they were also beautiful. They possessed that quality which arises from a nicely adjusted sense of use on the one hand, and adornment on the other; and in addition to being suited to their purpose, they were ornamental. There was no conscious striving after effect, and the materials were fashioned with due regard to their nature, the results being raised from the commonplace by such touches of taste as were conceived best by the worker. Very gratifying to the eye were many of the designs, excellent examples of manipulative skill.

Tradition was strong in influencing metalwork, as it was in other branches of village craft. Through generations seeking for improvement, by long periods of use, patterns and executive methods were perfected. The origin of many utensils and implements, that became the ordinary adjuncts of the home, was traceable to needs of long ago. Full of suggestion are the very names—the chimney-crane, the roasting-jack, rush-light holders, and the rest — recalling to mind olden ways of living that have now been superseded. Local types developed in metalwork, just as they did in building. The blacksmithing of Kent and Sussex had certain distinctions; there was a special pattern for casements in Berkshire; while the district around Chipping Campden, in Gloucestershire, had its particular form of casement-fastener. North, south, east and west of England little variations and singularities occur

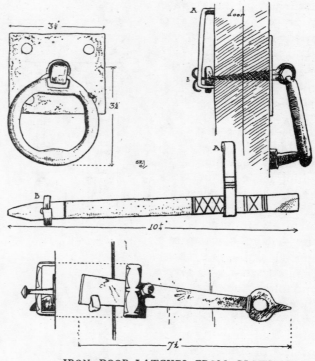

IRON DOOR-LATCHES FROM GLOUCESTER-SHIRE AND WARWICKSHIRE

129

in objects that were common to all parts. Localities now-a-days are losing their distinguishing marks. Those things to which the village worker once gave his thought are now but rarely made, and only occasionally one has the good fortune to meet a smith who knows the old patterns and can make them. The treasures that used to adorn the cottages have mostly been acquired by collectors, or distributed in other ways. But interesting and curious objects are still to be found among the heterogeneous possessions of villagers, some of real old local work, some obviously from other parts.

Metalwork in cottages falls under two heads, viz. :—that which was fitted or fixed to the buildings, and that which was movable. To the first-named group belong door and window fittings. The entrance door, often accentuated by the surrounding structural brickwork, timbers, or masonry, was given further importance by the ironwork with which it was adorned ; hinges, latches, bolts, handles, or arranged nail-heads, added to the effect. Many are examples of true smithing, honest in execution, suited to their purpose, and not unpleasing in form. Handles and knockers of simple wrought ironwork from Worcestershire, Herefordshire, Gloucestershire, Essex, Surrey and Shropshire, are shown on page 131, and may be considered typical specimens. Many latches and bolts were decorated with incised patterns, such as are seen in the illustration on this page, and in the door-latches shown on page 129 ; it was a style of enrichment generally practised, and peculiar to no particular district. That the old workers were

not wanting in a sense of grace is demonstrated by the refinement, of the good latch from Warwickshire, fellow to the one above-mentioned, on page 129 ; and on this page, by the shaping of the back-plates that carry the bolts.

Window-casements, to which leaded lights were fixed, and the necessary fittings for their adjustment, were objects for the village blacksmith's special skill. To them his best work was given and much fine smithcraft may still be seen. Always strongly lighted from behind, and showing more or less in silhouette, the well-designed shapes were aptly placed.

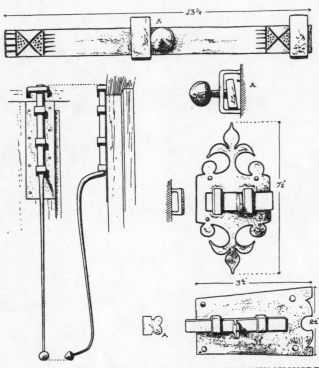

IRON DOOR-BOLTS FROM WARWICKSHIRE

130

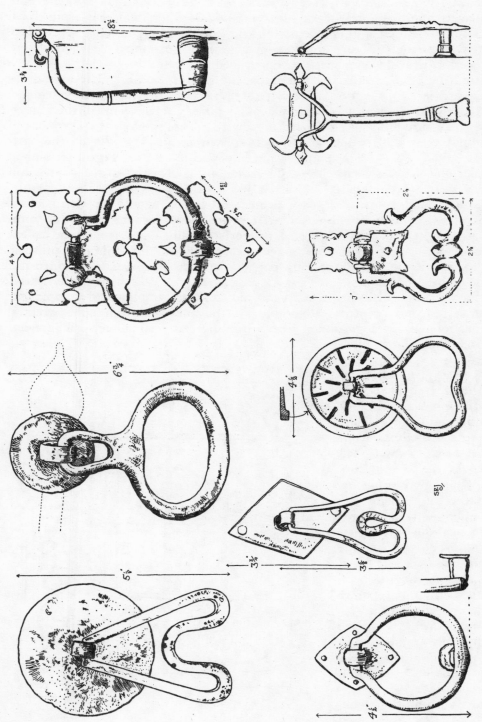

IRON DOOR-HANDLES AND KNOCKERS FROM WORCESTERSHIRE, HERE-
FORDSHIRE, GLOUCESTERSHIRE, ESSEX, SURREY AND SHROPSHIRE

Two complete casements are shown, one from Marston Magna, in Somerset (opposite), having an uncommon fastening, and one from East Hendred (on this page), representing the Berkshire type, with scrolls too lightly constructed for long service. Spring casement-fasteners from Worcestershire and Somerset are reproduced opposite.

Around the open fireplace circled the life of the home. The chimney-crane, utilitarian in its motive, was treated as a decorative centrepiece for the cavernous depth of the fireplace opening. It was embellished in a strong and suitable way, and with a view to its constant proximity to fire. Chimney-cranes often furnish instances of extraordinary ability on the part of the smith. A fine specimen from Sussex appears on page 134, and a simpler one, from a farmhouse at Churchill, in Worcestershire, on the same page; it will be observed that each has two movements. The movable accessories, dogs, pots, fireirons, footmen and trivets, would be within convenient reach. One of the wrought-iron fire-dogs given on page 134, from Kingston, in the Isle of Wight, has supports for spits; and the other, called cup or posset-dog, has an arrangement at the top for holding tankards or mugs. Fire-irons of various patterns appear on pages 135 and 136. Some are of traditional smith's work; others, from Wiltshire, are brightly polished and adorned with those vase-shaped forms so commonly employed in the eighteenth century. Notable are the tongs with branched terminations for moving logs, and the beautiful pierced iron shovel. The iron

footman and fender, illustrated on page 135, are good examples of pierced and hammered ironwork. On the same page is a reproduction of an unusual object, a fire-cover, from Lancashire. It was used to cover the fire at Curfew, when, by custom introduced in William the Conqueror's days, all fires were put out and lights extinguished. The one exemplified is of brass, the patterns having been beaten up on separate strips and riveted on.

Other utensils that were in daily use are shown on page 137. Dip and rush-light - holders stood on the floor or were suspended from the wall. Two of those illustrated are standards with metal

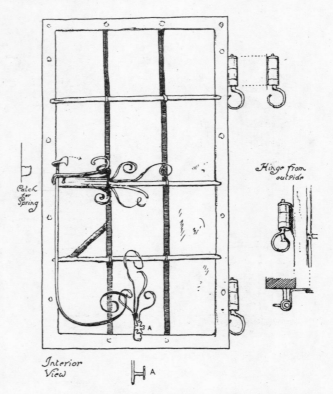

WINDOW-CASEMENT FROM BERKSHIRE

132

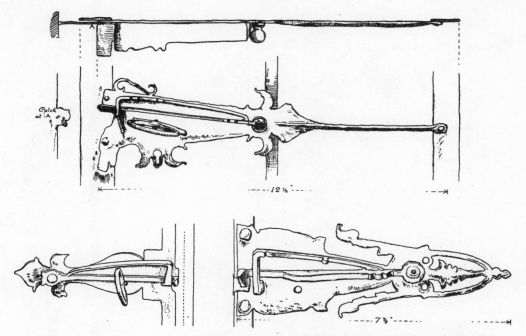

SPRING CASEMENT-FASTENERS FROM WORCESTER-
SHIRE AND SOMERSETSHIRE

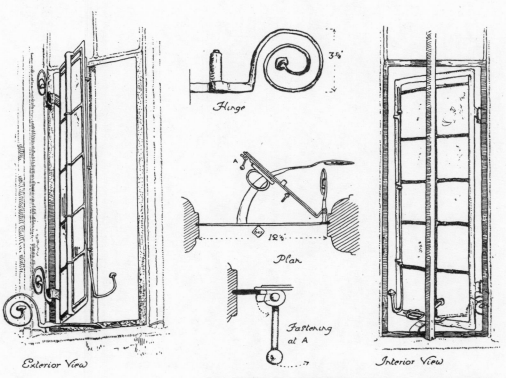

WINDOW-CASEMENT FROM SOMERSETSHIRE

133

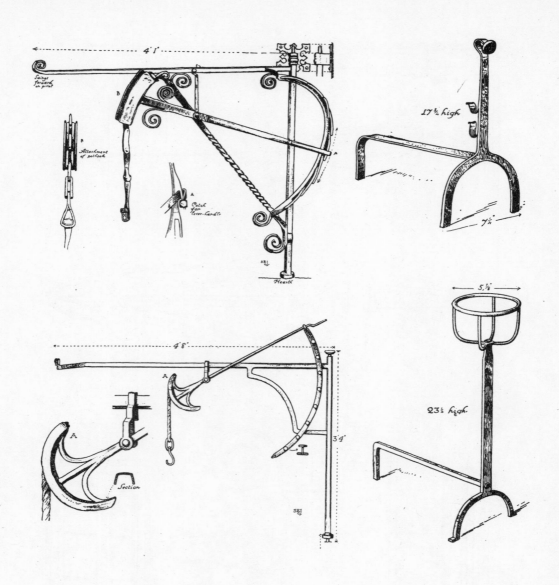

IRON KITCHEN-CRANES FROM SUSSEX AND WORCESTERSHIRE
AND FIRE-DOGS FROM THE ISLE OF WIGHT AND SUSSEX

134

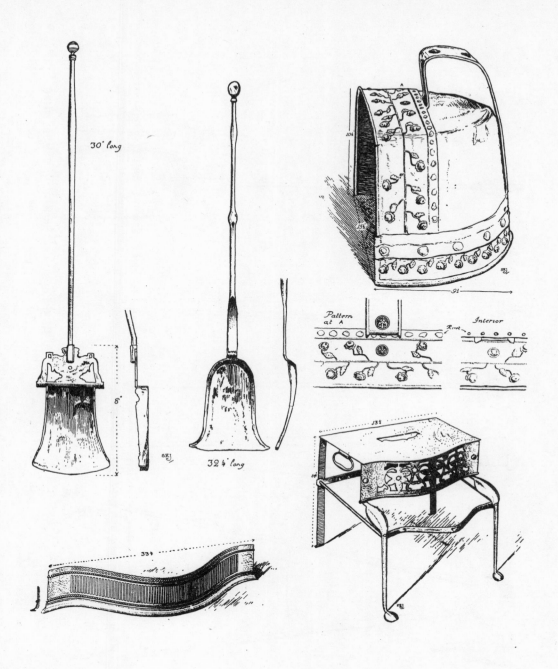

30" long

32¾ long

IRON FIRE-SHOVELS FROM SUSSEX AND DERBYSHIRE, BRASS FIRE-COVER
FROM LANCASHIRE, AND IRON FENDER AND FOOTMAN FROM SUSSEX

135

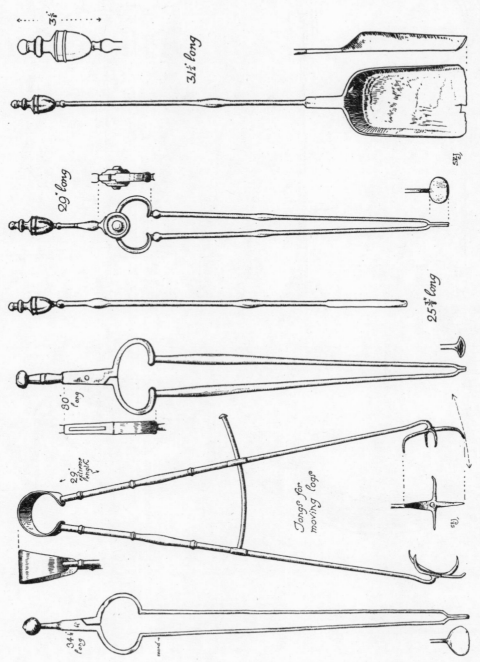

FIRE-IRONS FROM SUSSEX AND WILTSHIRE

31½ long

3⁵⁄₈

29 long

25⅞ long

30 long

29 extreme length

Tongs for moving logs

34¼ long

136

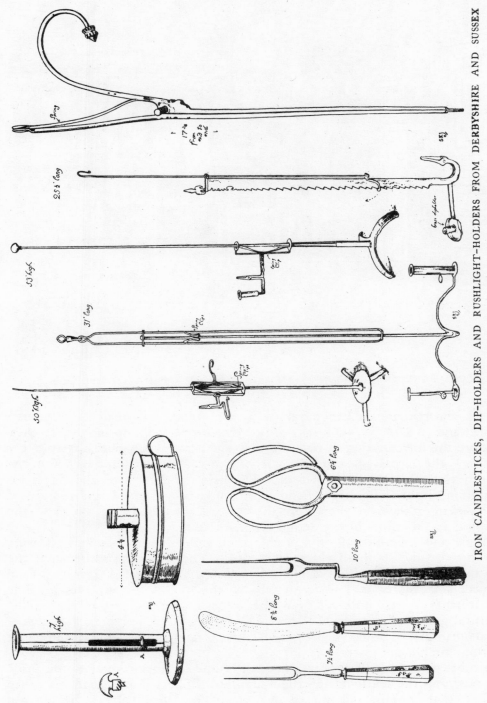

IRON CANDLESTICKS, DIP-HOLDERS AND RUSHLIGHT-HOLDERS FROM DERBYSHIRE AND SUSSEX
IRON SCISSORS, BRAND-TONGS, KNIFE AND FORKS FROM SUSSEX

137

STOKE ALBANY, NORTHAMPTONSHIRE

bases, and two are for hanging; in all cases the actual holders are adjustable, and would be held in position by means of a spring or ratchet. Before the introduction of matches the tinder-box was a necessity to every home; the circular box at the base of the round hand-candlestick in the illustration, the lid of which is movable, held the flint, steel, and tinder for obtaining light. The right-hand specimen, a pair of iron brand-tongs used for picking glowing embers from the fire to light tobacco, is tooled at the angles, and the lines of the design are admirable.

Simple and unambitious, the products of the village woodworkers were strong, useful, and not lacking in beauty. The craftsmen appreciated the nature of the material in which they worked, and the character of each object was more or less suggested by the quality of the wood. The treatment of oak differed from that of ash, and ash from elm. The natural grain and texture of the woods, not obscured, heightened effects of craftsmanship. Sound construction was a controlling factor, and gave forms suitable and good.

In times gone by, villagers treasured their fine old furniture and took pride in retaining the heirlooms of their families. There is still good reason to think that certain old pieces seen have descended from father to son through a long period. But such is not generally the case, and it is now

138

Panel Moulding

OAK CRADLE FROM GLOUCESTERSHIRE, OAK JOINT-STOOLS FROM SOMERSET-
SHIRE AND GLOUCESTERSHIRE, AND OAK CHAIR FROM WARWICKSHIRE

ASH CHAIR AND OAK ARM-CHAIR FROM WARWICKSHIRE

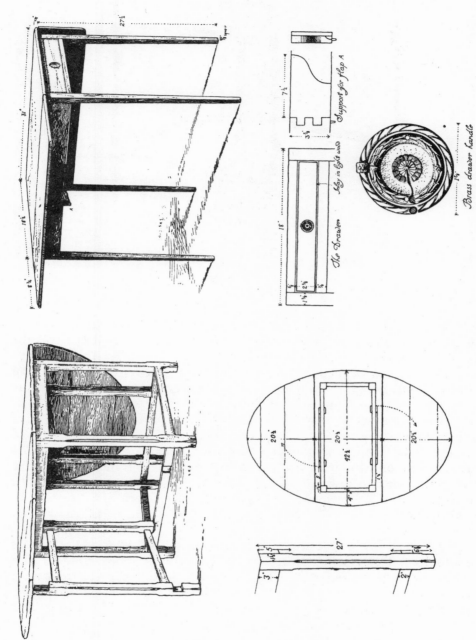

27½

7½

3½

Support for flap A

18

Key in flap end

The Drawer

2½

Brass drawer handle

1¾

20½

20½

20½

92½

27

3

6¼

OAK GATE-LEG TABLE FROM DERBYSHIRE AND MAHOGANY
TABLE WITH TWO FLAPS AND DRAWER

OAK TABLE FROM GLOUCESTERSHIRE

rare to find old dressers, chairs, and tables—such as those at Stoke Albany, in Northamptonshire (page 138), which have now been distributed—in the places they have occupied for years past.

Oaken furniture was pegged together with oak pins, a system of fastening that warded off decay. Joint-stools, so constructed, were at one time frequently to be found in the villages. Two examples of the familiar seventeenth century type, from Ditcheat, Somersetshire, and Whittington, Gloucestershire, are given on page 139 ; each has a carved top rail and turned legs. The oak arm-chair on page 140 has arms of a pattern that was usual, and on the back rails and legs are gouged incisions. Very similar is the chair shown on page 139, but it lacks the arms ; both examples are from Warwickshire. An ash chair, with traverse bars or different widths at the back and a turned front rail, is illustrated on page 140.

On page 141 is shown a gate-leg table from Derbyshire, obviously of village workmanship. The oval top is in three pieces and has two hinged flaps secured to the fixed centrepiece. The oak table on this page, fitted with a drawer, was found in a secluded cottage on the borders of Gloucestershire, and has the characteristics of seventeenth century work. Of a much later date is the mahogany table appearing on page 141, and it demonstrates how another style of work was evolved to suit a different kind of wood. The support beneath the flap has a wooden hinge that works round a wooden pin, while the brass drawer-handle is of graceful design.

Chests, for domestic or other purposes, have had a long association with village life. The parish chest, kept within the church, was often a fine

142

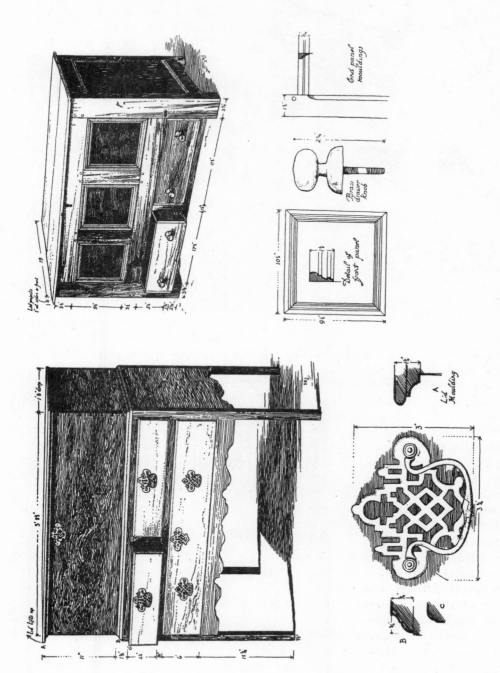

143

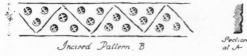

Incised Pattern. B

Section at A

OAK CLOTHES-HUTCH FROM
BUCKINGHAMSHIRE

and elaborate piece or craft-work. The linen-chest, or clothes-hutch, of the cottager was made on more simple lines; the flat top served as a seat. Some chests were carved on front and ends, but more often they were plain, or merely panelled, as are the Buckinghamshire examples on pages 143 and 144. Handles and lockplates, when of brass, contrasted brightly with the wood. The appearance of the oak chest with drawers (page 143) is enhanced by the brass fittings; while the teak chest (opposite) is strengthened with brass plates at the angles, and decorated with brass studs on the lid. The small carved box shown below comes from Wooferton, in Herefordshire, and has an iron lockplate and

hinges, and ivory inlay on the lid. It was, no doubt, originally used as a bible-box, a usual possession of old country people. Miscellaneous objects of cottage furniture are the two mahogany framed looking-glasses, illustrated on page 145, and the oak cradle from Gloucestershire (page 139), provided with a hood, and apparently belonging to the latter part of the seventeenth century. Structural fittings, the work of the carpenter, were sensibly contrived. The wooden window-seat, made in the thickness of the wall, rose as a flap, and opened to view a roomy box beneath. Over the open-

CARVED OAK BOX FROM HEREFORDSHIRE

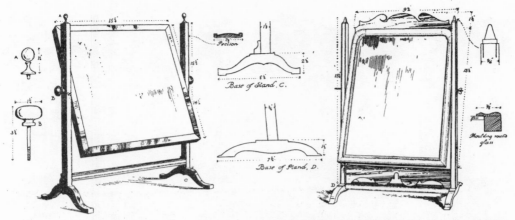

MAHOGANY FRAMED LOOKING-GLASSES

ing of the fire-place, and extending from it to the ceiling, would sometimes be a spit-rack to hold the polished spits. An example, from Warnham in Sussex, is given on page 146. Both members of the rack project five inches from the wall, and are ornamented with simple cut-out work. The old pattern ledged door—consisting of upright boards fastened to horizontal ledges—with its iron latch and strap-hinges, always looked appropriate to its place. This method of construction fortunately still survives in country places.

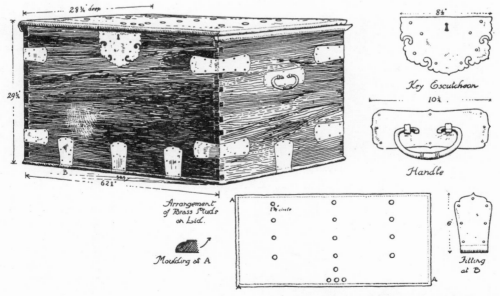

TEAK CHEST WITH BRASS FITTINGS

145

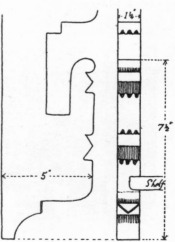

1½"

7½"

Shelf

5"

SPIT-RACK FROM WARNHAM, SUSSEX

146

DIVISION VII

GARDENS

VII.—GARDENS.

OTTAGE gardening is a subject difficult to define and include within certain limits. In the practice of it English villagers have always excelled. Rural occupations, indeed, have ever appealed to the national mind, and whether the consideration be of gardens that surround mansions, houses, or peasants' dwellings, the same evidence of devotion to "the purest of human pleasures" is there. In the best of our village gardens the effects appear to be spontaneous and unstudied, and the operations of art are cunningly concealed; they seem to have grown together without the aid of man. Villagers are born gardeners. With skill they apply and adapt their knowledge acquired from nature. "The very labourer," said Washington Irving, "with his thatched cottage and narrow slip of ground, attends to their embellishment. The trim hedge, the grass-plot before the door, the little flower-bed bordered with snug box, the woodbine trained up against the wall, and hanging its blossoms about the lattice, the plot of flowers in the window, the holly, providentially planted about the house, to cheat winter of its dreariness, and to throw in a semblance of green summer to cheer the fireside : all these bespeak the influence of taste, flowing down from high sources, and pervading the lowest levels of the public mind."

It is in their ordered arrangement that old cottage gardens excel. An intuitive faculty on the part of their makers gave results for the repetition of which it is impossible to lay down definite laws. The charm of many gardens, such as the one at Shepreth, in Cambridgeshire (page 151), is beyond analysis, and their attractiveness is due to the personal influence of those who have cared for them ; villagers felt what was right to do, and ideas came naturally through intimate association with the soil. That is as it should be ; gardens, as houses, ought to reflect the personality of their owners. The vegetable beds, in which lay the real, material value of the cottage gardens, were tended as carefully as the plots given up to flowers. Between the narrow paths would be rows of beans, peas, cabbages, and roots, with here and there an old-fashioned fruit tree and bushes of

HANWELL, OXFORDSHIRE

149

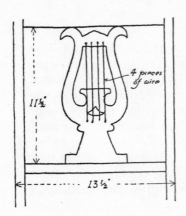

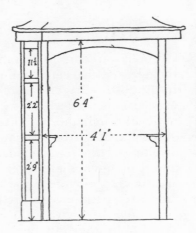

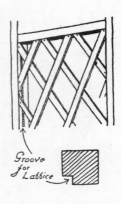

currants and gooseberries. In shady places rhubarb flourished and nuts were near the boundary hedge. Near to the house flowers bloomed

and their fragrance was wafted within. Little front gardens bordered the road, a joy for the passer-by.

The cleft oak fencing that enclosed so many old gardens always looked well and was very durable. It is now, unfortunately, usually replaced by machine-cut oak or larch. Where walls were used for boundary divisions, they partook of the manner of the buildings they surrounded, and there was thus an affinity between each. Wiltshire garden walls, like those of the cottages, were of cob, and flint, and brick, and stone. Two, from Winterbourne Dantsey and Upper Woodford, in Wiltshire, are illustrated on page 155; each is protected from the weather by thatching, most picturesquely applied. A

150

GREAT CHESTERFORD, ESSEX

SHEPRETH, CAMBRIDGESHIRE

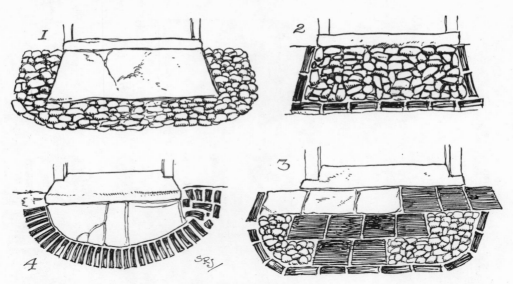

PAVINGS IN FRONT OF DOORWAYS IN OXFORDSHIRE

stone wall from Hanwell, in Oxfordshire (page 149), is rich with mosses, and above are cut box trees and laurels. At Winterbourne Gunner, in Wiltshire (opposite), the gateway has been effectively treated, and the thatching of the wall continues over the oak-framed opening. In Yorkshire the piers at each side of gates are each of one stone only. The cottage at Nether Compton, in Dorset (page 157), is approached by a flight of stone steps, and two cut yews border the way. The entrance path was frequently paved with the handiest material the locality afforded, and many charming effects in stone, bricks, and cobbles may be seen. There is a beautiful garden at Alhampton, in Somersetshire (page 158), luxuriant with flowers in the summer-time ; it has a stone-paved way and flower-beds edged with upright stones. Other simple methods of paving are shown by the illustrations from Oxfordshire, on this page, and Upper Boddington, Northamptonshire (page 154) ; they are carried out in stone, old narrow bricks, quarries, and cobbles. The original of the porch given on page 150 is at Great Chesterford, in Essex, and is painted green, which shows effectively against the white plaster wall.

Yew trees have from time out of mind been associated with English villages. They were commonly planted in churchyards—fitting places for trees that were regarded as emblems of immortality. At the festival of Easter they used to furnish greenery for the decoration of the churches. But yew trees were not confined to churchyards. In squires' gardens they were trained and cut ; they bordered shady walks and bowers. Village gardens, too, had their clipped work in yew and box, and much of it can still be seen. It is generally limited to the shaping of one or two trees and there is little attempt at formal arrangement. Yew trees that have been cut into fantastic shapes, such as those at Upper Boddington, in Northamptonshire (page 159), are exceptional, and the usual forms are of simple outline.

WINTERBOURNE GUNNER, WILTSHIRE

153

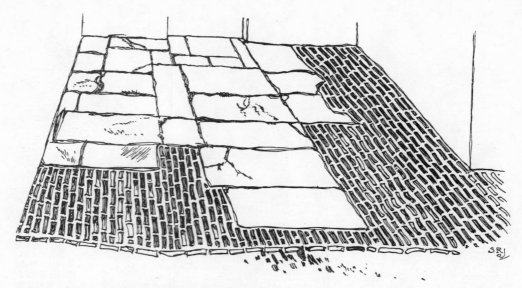

PAVING IN FRONT OF DOORWAY AT UPPER
BODDINGTON, NORTHAMPTONSHIRE

Two at Glaston, in Rutland (page 160), help to seclude the cottage from the
high-road ; and a series of circular shrubs edge the walk at Therfield, in
Hertfordshire (page 156).   The two box trees that guard the stone-paved
entrance way at Mollington, in Oxfordshire (page 161), are well cut and
effectively placed.   They, and the adjoining box hedges, give colour to the
group.   Another Oxfordshire example is the box tree, trained close to the
stone wall, at Hanwell (page 160).   The deep green of these trees afford
excellent backgrounds for the display of flowers.   Some allege that yews
and box harbour insects and pests, deprive plants growing near of nutriment,
and make the successful growing of flowers in close proximity an impossi-
bility.   But that cannot be always so, for flowers in such positions in cottage
gardens flourish amazing-
ly.   No more charming
country sight can be seen
than a clipped peacock,
or some other quaintly
cut device in yew, with
flower-beds around, en-
closed by short lengths of
box edging. Here flowers
come and go as seasons
pass; snowdrops, crocuses,
yellow daffodils, prim-
roses, sweet-scented gilli-
flowers, early tulips and
violets. With the ad-
vancing season come the

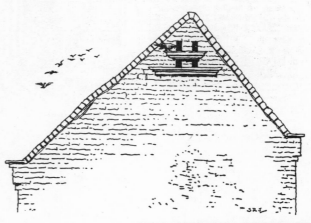

LONG MARSTON, YORKSHIRE

154

THATCHED GARDEN-WALLS IN WILTSHIRE

155

THERFIELD, HERTFORDSHIRE

columbines, pinks, roses, and the brave show of summer blossom, and autumn days are rich with fragrance.

Pigeons circle round many village homes, harmful for the seeds, perhaps, but pleasant to see. Cottagers used to keep them, and provision was sometimes made in old buildings for sheltering the birds. The upper part of the brick gable at Long Marston, in Yorkshire (page 154), served for a pigeon house; the perches are of stone. On south walls of cottages sundials were sometimes placed. The Yorkshire example, from Dent (page 163), is situated over an entrance porch and surrounded by ivy. At Alhampton, in Somersetshire (page 38), the dial is contained on a rectangular stone which is affixed to the gable point. Before the days of watches and clocks, sundials were the countryman's only mode of counting time. The sunlight marked the fleeting hours; on dull and lowering days the passage of time was unrecorded. "I count only the hours that are serene" was graven on a dial-plate at which Hazlitt pictured a studious monk looking on sunny days. And peaceful thoughts, such as are contained in the words of this inscription, do old sundials suggest; they bring to mind pictures of a calm and easy-going past. As time goes by, the old cottages and their trim gardens continue to add beauty to the countryside. The garden gates, as in days of long ago, open on to narrow paths that lead to those ancient structures, the village homes of England, changeless objects amid a changing world.

SYDNEY R. JONES.

NETHER COMPTON, DORSETSHIRE

157

ALHAMPTON, SOMERSETSHIRE

158

UPPER BODDINGTON, NORTHAMPTONSHIRE

159

GLASTON, RUTLAND

HANWELL, OXFORDSHIRE

160

MOLLINGTON, OXFORDSHIRE

161

WILBARSTON, NORTHAMPTONSHIRE
162

DENT, YORKSHIRE

C000229860

WILL STEWART

JUST
SURVIVE
[SOMEHOW]

EVERYTHING YOU NEED TO
KNOW TO SUCCEED IN YOUR
FIRST YEAR IN BUSINESS

R^ethink

First published in Great Britain in 2021
by Rethink Press (www.rethinkpress.com)

All the author's profits from the sale of this book will be donated to the Samaritans

CONTENTS

For Zoe

Through the blood, the sweat, the tears,
the pain and the despair.

Through the bounce.

Through the buzz, the delirium, the glory,
the paradise and the near nirvana.

Through the wobble and the crash.

Through the groundhog rinse and repeat.

Through it all... you always had my back.

x

FOREWORD

I remember getting my head out of the rugby scrum just in time to see the ball being bulleted down the line. Until it got to Will with a poor pass, arriving down by his toes. He got his hands to it but knocked it forward. The referee blew his whistle. All the forwards trudged back to the site of the knock-on. It was so annoying when that happened. All that effort to secure a clean ball only for it to be wasted. I caught Will's eye. We both knew it was the quality of the pass rather than his hands that were the issue but neither of us said anything.

We set up again. We won the scrum again. The ball was fizzed along the line and out to Will. Another poor pass, but this time Will had anticipated what was coming. He caught it down by his laces, straightened up and drove over the gain line with strength and power, setting us up to build on his attack. He'd immediately learned from the previous failure and bounced straight back. With resilience.

That's the first thing that comes to mind when I think about Will. Resilience. That's one of the main reasons this book is so good. Will is a survivor and *Just Survive Somehow* bottles that brilliantly. It comes as no surprise to me whatsoever that he has made a huge success of his business even in the middle of a pandemic.

I've known Will Stewart for 33 years. At school it was rugby that bound us. We had different friendship circles and I was just a bit too naughty. He was sporty, academic and intelligent. He was prefect material – I was not. He didn't dump the free papers he was delivering as his first job into a skip, I did. Morals in business are a choice, says Will. He is utterly right. Despite our differences as young men, we forged a deep friendship, and we have grown closer and closer over the decades, particularly as our interest in leadership has increased, alongside our depth of understanding in the concept.

It's in our leadership philosophy that we find the red thread that runs through us both. Our true north: it's all about kindness. And purpose. Not in a soft, ineffective way – but with rigour and resilience, the courage to do the right thing for colleagues, customers and community. If you look after your people, then they will look after the customers and the business.

Making money isn't evil, it's what you do with it that matters. I learned that from experience and from Will. Wherever possible you should dedicate your career to doing something that matters, it's an enormous privilege to be able to leave a legacy through your work but if you look closely enough then there's opportunity to do so in every role. Kindness underpins that.

If you're thinking of going it alone in the business world, this book will act as a checklist for you. And who doesn't want a checklist in their life? It will also challenge what you think is important. For Will and me, it's critical that we challenge our assumptions and seek other perspectives. You never learn otherwise.

Finally, this book is about resilience and strategy, innovation and bravery. It's also all about leadership, learning and purpose, but it is so much more too.

Joel Mitchell MA BA BSc
Managing Director, Stagecoach South East

INTRODUCTION

Is it random chance or a particular sequence of events that has led to you to this book?

I hope you have a fantastic business idea that feels like an itch that won't go away. I hope that you are already deep into the planning phase to turn that idea into reality, that you know you will regret it forever if you don't take the leap and give it a go. This book will help you as things begin to happen, showing you what you need to do more of and less of to make your business vision real.

It's probable that I don't know you personally, but I believe I can make some fair assumptions. You are likely to:

- ✧ Be aged between fourteen and ninety.
- ✧ Have always had a desire to start your own business.
- ✧ Have run out of excuses not to take action as your mates are bored of hearing you talk about your ideas.
- ✧ Have started budgeting and planning how much your idea will cost.
- ✧ Be driven, brave, ambitious and resilient.
- ✧ Have identified a point of difference and developed a vision and clear purpose that you can succinctly communicate to your audience.
- ✧ Be a good leader of people.
- ✧ Be passionate beyond belief.

❖ Cope well with stress (see Chapter 8).

❖ Create time like magic.

❖ Embrace change like nobody else you know.

Does this sound like you? If so, read on, my friend, I have some valuable advice for you. And if it's not a full set of yeses to these points yet, fear not. I can help you, too.

Do you have a business plan? To be honest, I didn't – a business plan is not essential. In my experience, starting up a business is a chaotic process, and plans and forecasts can become obsolete overnight. A detailed business plan may be important for you, but passion and resilience are much more useful.

You cannot choose the environment you were born into, but you can certainly use that environment, its circumstance and opportunities to change your life for the better. That is what I set out to do in September 2014 when I took the leap off the cliff and moved from planning and talking about my startup idea to actually doing it. I gave my notice to my employer and set a date to start trading.

We all need luck to survive in business. You and I have all the luck we need for three reasons:

1. We are alive today and not at any time in the past. Even through traumatic global events, we are better equipped to survive than any generation before us.

2. We are literate, educated, relatively healthy and safe.

3. The modern world, particularly easily accessible technology, has given us all the opportunity we require to start our own business.

The other critical ingredient in success is hard work. The two go hand in hand. I discovered early on that the harder I worked, the luckier I became. Working harder than anyone else is going to make the biggest difference when you take the leap.

I have built a business from scratch that is completely self-funded, has no debt, has been profitable since inception and achieved the milestone turnover of £1 million in Year Three. I then grew that business to hit a turnover of over £3 million in Year Four. And it is still growing today.

Sir Richard Branson's advice to keep meticulous notes about the ups and downs of my working week, and crucially what I would have done differently, has been invaluable.[1] It has led to a lot of notebooks accumulating in the spare room and under the stairs over my first years in business. I make notes the old-school way with pen and paper at least once a week. They are a mixture of to-do lists, reflections and even doodles. My notebook habit (consistently reviewing the notes as well as writing them) was only intended to help me (and most won't mean much to anyone else), but they now add up to a picture of my process over the first years of my business, as it was happening.

I want this book to be real, as current as my latest notebook and relevant to where you are now in your startup journey. Particularly in the early years, the possibility of failure is always on the horizon. That's not a bad thing and you have to learn to lick the sticky fingers of failure many times. Fear of failure can be crippling, and I intend to help you overcome that fear.

---

1   R Branson, *Losing My Virginity* (Virgin Books, 2009)

I didn't start my own business with the goal of making millions – that never works. For me, it was never about the money. It was about the change I could make, the difference I could make to my life and other people's. Since I launched my startup, I have become rich in ways I hadn't imagined when I began, which feels miles more satisfying than watching the millions stack up. I have everything I need in life, and that means I have everything to lose as well. That thought stays with me every day and provides me with the survival instinct we all need to keep the rollercoaster rolling.

In *Just Survive Somehow*, I will share the learnings, scary facts and gems of advice buried in the rubble of my notebooks with you. In a world full of posts, memes and supershort video content, all designed to be consumed at speed, there is something almost romantic about reading words on a page and taking time to absorb them.

Starting a business will change your life, so it's a good idea to take advice from the experts. Before I started my business, I read a lot of relevant books by people who had gone before me. I have added a recommended reading list at the end of this book so that you can benefit from the wisdom of these experts, too. All of them helped me in some way, but I've highlighted the books that made a particular difference.

Just Survive Somehow will tell you everything you need to do before you start your business to hit the ground running and give yourself the best chance of success. It will go on to tell you everything you need to do to get through the first year of your startup. If you're in a hurry, you'll find a cheat sheet at the end of each chapter which summarises the content and (hopefully) entices you to read on, but for maximum return on investment, I recommend you take in all the advice *Just Survive Somehow* has to offer.

Before we start, a word of warning: *Just Survive Somehow* is going to be an honest read. 'Fuck' is my favourite word, so if you don't like swearing, sorry. But if you are planning to survive your first year in business, I can guarantee you too will soon be saying it a lot. Or perhaps 'fiddlesticks' would suit you better...

You have one simple task: *Just Survive Somehow.*

Let us begin.

1

WHAT YOU
ALREADY KNOW

Every job you have ever done, whether you loved it or couldn't stand it, has shaped you and brought you closer to where you are today, on the brink of starting your own business. In other words, every job has taught you something.

In this chapter, I'll show you how I was led from my first pocket-money job towards taking the leap into my startup. Think back through the employers you've had and take some time to consider what each one has taught you. Write a list of every job you've ever done, starting with your Saturday job as a teenager, and make notes on what you learned, even if it was simply that you did not want to work there longer than absolutely necessary, and why. My own notes will show you the level of detail that is useful.

My work history

Job 1: Paper round

I don't mind admitting, I hated this job, but I learned that you need money if you want to buy stuff, and to get money, you need to work hard. I was introduced to professional morals – I would never dream of dumping the free papers I was delivering in a skip and still collect my wage – and persistence – all those front doors with signs stating 'No local papers' never put me off.

> Key learning: Choose to have morals in business.

Job 2: Lab assistant

My mother got me a summer job in the lab where she worked, mostly sticking labels on little bottles of medicines before they were sent out to pharmacies. Oh, the frustration of picking the strange gluey deposits off the bottles when I hadn't attached the sticker in the right place! But just like riding a bike, once you learn how to fail well, it's with you for life.

> Key learning: Fail quickly. If something's wrong at the start, accept it, own it and move on.

Job 3: Bar worker

I worked in three different pubs that had one thing in common: they were all hovels. Serving overpriced booze to drunks, I earned £3.12 an hour. I was ecstatic when it rose to £3.22. I needed the money to go travelling, but these were rubbish jobs for rubbish employers.

Key learning: Time is more valuable than money. If you really hate a job, don't waste your precious time on being miserable.

Job 4: Loft ladder salesman

I was lucky: I went to university before the days of student fees and loans, and I even got a grant. Two amazing lecturers helped me find an eight-week placement with a small business through the Shell Graduate Enterprise Scheme. This gave me a taste of office life and business operations, and the chance to learn from an owner who fought for every penny.

Selling loft ladders provided personal and professional lightbulb moments for me. Listening to and learning from the company's two salespeople: their approach, their patter, their script, I discovered that I could sell and, crucially, that sales are the substance of running a business. We are all salespeople; we are always selling, always pitching. If you can sell, genuinely and authentically, then your business has a significant advantage and high chance of success.

During my time selling loft ladders, a newspaper marketing campaign I ran generated leads, and before I knew it, I was upgrading customers from deluxe to concertina like a pro. As the great saying* goes: 'If you can sell loft ladders, you can sell anything'. (*Nobody ever said this.)

Key learning: You are always selling.

Job 5: Promotions analyst

This was the first job I actually liked, working for an inspirational, funny and caring boss. I was only crunching numbers on spreadsheets for a well-known supermarket chain, but it was a great office environment.

It was my first experience of working in a big organisation where everyone did things properly, and I met some amazingly talented buyers. Returning from a visit to the biscuit buyer with an enormous box of Jaffa Cakes was a highlight. I arrived back in the marketing department like a king with the spoils of war.

It was also my first experience of sitting opposite someone all day and the weird, self-conscious time of getting used to looking at them and them looking at me. And I had to learn to answer the phone professionally. Crucially, that job gave me a goal: I wanted to be a buyer, ideally a biscuit buyer.

Key learning: Get a job doing something you are passionate about.

Job 6: Assistant store manager

After a year travelling, I landed straight from the Indonesian jungle on to the sales floor of Woolworths in Staines High Street. It was a shock to the system.

The coalface of retail is incredibly hard work, particularly at Christmas. I worked brutal fourteen-hour days and my feet ached like I never thought possible. It was frantic, chaotic mayhem. How did so much stuff get sold and so much money made?

I remember the office manager allowing me to hold £25,000 in used banknotes in each hand before going to the bank and feeling the buzz of money. Life and work are not about money, but it does give you options, and for that fleeting moment, I was the richest I had ever been.

Public-facing workplaces are full of dramatic incidents: serious robbery, staff being threatened, a woman collapsing in the automatic doors, power cuts, and so much shoplifting. There was a Robbie Williams lyric at the time about learning to shoplift at Woolies, which didn't help. Woolworths was a huge learning curve, full of thrills and surprises.

Key learning: Sitting down at a desk to work is a privilege.

Job 7: Space planner

Planograms, dimensions and range planning were fairly dull day to day, but this was my first experience of working in an entrepreneurial team, making quick decisions, learning and failing fast.

> Key learning: Not making a decision is worse than making the wrong decision.

Job 8: Pricing manager

I learned so much about capacity and delivery here, it made me realise that if I worked 50% more hours than the next person, I would get 50% more experience. In two years' calendar time, I could accrue three years' experience. That concept has stayed with me ever since.

> Key learning: Be the hardest worker in the room.

Job 9: Assistant buyer

At last, my first foray into buying after my eighth interview for an assistant buyer role. I had been ready to give up after the seventh failure; luckily, the persistence I gained on my paper round served me well. As the role would involve the buying of babywear, I got to know every pregnant lady in the company to learn about what the customers wanted, even though I didn't understand the products I was sourcing until my twins were born in 2016.

Key learning: Resilience.

Job 10: Junior buyer

I was still working for Woolworths, but the company was slowly dying by now. This had a plus side, though: it meant there were increasing opportunities for me to grow my career as large numbers of staff were leaving.

If you are good and hardworking at your job, you will always be able to open doors. I remember my head of buying realising in May that nobody had bought that season's sun-care range. I put my hand up and offered to call L'Oréal to see if we could stock that year's market-leading product. We became one of the top five stockists of the brand that summer.

Key learning: When growing your career, always volunteer.

Job 11: Buyer

This was a significant milestone: I had become a fully fledged buyer for Woolworths' Homeware and Gift department.

Actually, I had been lackadaisical about applying for this role. Worn down after months of unsuccessful interviews for similar jobs, I had been told that this job had been given to another junior buyer, and that only women could buy for that department, so I didn't push for it. Then an encouraging chat in the corridor with the recruiting manager (who went on to be a huge influence on my career) ended with me applying for my dream job and being given the freedom to change everything. In the space of an hour, my work life had flipped. My boss was a legend. I had learned to grasp opportunity, ignore the doubters and believe in myself, although it did help when someone more senior did, too.

Key learning: Never, ever give up.

Job 12: Senior buyer

I never did end up buying biscuits, but I got promoted to the biggest confectionery buying job in Europe – another pinch-me moment. Still working for Woolworths, I had a big team and massive budget, and I needed to use them both to stop the supermarkets from destroying us.

I was always the type of buyer who needed to try the product before having an opinion, so I ignored all the dieticians and nutritionists for six months and ate only confectionery. My team and I were developing exclusives, launching major innovations and bringing new brands to the market. It was the most incredible fun – I could bribe any department to get stuff done. Believe me, turning up on the IT floor with 120 dark chocolate Yorkies will influence the type of laptop you will get.

Key learning: Incentives get results.

Job 13: Business development manager

I had seven interviews before I finally got to work for John Lewis, but it was so worth it. Not only would I meet my future wife at 'the Partnership', but I would also position myself as a credible, authentic professional with a socially progressive attitude working for a company that was built on purpose and values.

My boss backed me and together we made huge changes. I never got my 'Totally Integrated Tabletop Solution' project signed off, but I was certainly able to make a difference. This was largely down to the fact that I was able to create and understand Excel spreadsheets.

Key learning: Analysis and strategy provide the answers to any questions. Spreadsheets are your friend.

Job 14: Buyer

An opportunity arose to work for a brilliant boss, who believed in me, in the men's shoes and travel goods department of John Lewis, so I went all in. I'd never bought shoes or luggage before, but I love learning new things, exploring new markets, meeting new people and developing new products.

If you treat people with respect, they will share their opinions. I love hearing ideas. A bit of free advice from someone you know, like, trust and respect are gold dust.

Key learning: Respect is an incredibly important leadership quality.

Job 15: Senior buyer

The bath shop was the perfect place for me to end my employment with John Lewis. It was a huge department and I had buying experience in this category, so I saw loads of areas where I could make an impact. There was plenty of product variety for me to get my teeth stuck into, which meant loads of travel.

The first year was tough, but once I had everything, particularly my team, in place, this job was probably the easiest ride I have had in my career. It was during this time that I finally got a taster of the joys of working from home.

One trouble with big corporate firms is that everyone has to have an opinion, so there will always be someone who tells you why you can't do something. After a while, I stopped asking for permission and just got on with what I thought was right.

If you get over 80% of the decisions you are responsible for right, then you are winning. When you get it wrong, admit your error, find the solution and tell them both to your manager. Even if you're running your own business, you might have to explain yourself to partners or investors.

By the end of my time at John Lewis, I knew that I didn't have a corporate mindset and couldn't follow rules. That helped with what happened next.

Key learning: Ask for forgiveness, not permission.

Job 16: Retail and brand director

I joined the licensing industry because by this point, I had a burning desire to start my own business in this field, and it makes perfect sense to learn your trade while someone else is paying the bills. And I had realised that retail was dying, even before the Covid-19 pandemic hit; the set-up costs and return on investment (ROI) are appalling in this sector, and I wanted to be successful.

The licensing industry is where a huge proportion of branded products are created and made. It's the process of transferring the brand values, equity, design and intellectual property of one brand to a new product category or service. Licensing has low barriers to entry and is built on networking and relationships. It was huge then, and it's still growing. From the first interview, I knew this was what I was going to do for the rest of my career.

The licensing agency I joined had an entrepreneurial feel to it; nobody ever said no to anything, which I loved, but they held people to account, which I also loved. There was a strong sales mentality throughout the company; the importance of bringing cash into the business was regularly hammered home.

I remember being told by a headhunter once that if you are a director by the age of thirty-five, you will be able to do anything in your future career. Turns out she was right, even though I was pretty much director in title only. This, I discovered, is the way small companies have to operate.

Key learning: Cash is king, believe in your ideas, never give up.

Job 17: Managing director

After two years of planning, I was ready to strike out on my own. I had followed the ideal route of working for a company in the same industry I would be operating in, I had learned and saved as much as I could, and now I wanted to learn some more.

I will be boss-free forevermore. I've had seventeen managers and bosses over the years, many of whom I call mentors and friends, but from now on, I will be on my own.

Recently, I wrote a 'Boss List', rating all my bosses out of ten and highlighting my top five. It was quite a cathartic exercise and something I recommend you do to help frame your experience and the professional influences that have made a difference to the person you have become over the years. I would do it during Year Zero of your business journey, which we will cover in the next chapter.

Key learning: You, and only you, can change your life.

I have a mug on my desk with the word *Rich* on it. I don't think I could define what would need to happen or how much money I'd need to make for me to actually describe myself as 'rich'. But when I think about it, I am already rich.

Time is more valuable than money. When you leave a job that does not satisfy you for the promised land, your life will become richer than it has ever been before.

CHEAT SHEET

In this chapter, we have covered some valuable concepts:

✧ Luck is always a factor in business, but the harder you work, the luckier you will be. Persistence and resilience are key when building a career, and crucial in a startup.

✧ Every job you have ever done will have taught you something, even if all you learned was what you *don't* want to do with your life.

✧ Think back through the jobs and bosses you have had and how they influenced your life. This will help you find the path to your destination, and make sure it is something you're passionate about.

✧ Incentives are great at getting results.

✧ Always treat people with respect, it is an essential leadership quality.

✧ Don't shy away from analysis and strategy, which can provide the answers to any problem.

❖   Be the person who is known for putting your hand up
    to volunteer, who isn't afraid to fail because you can
    come up with the solution.

❖   When you decide on the industry that is the perfect
    fit for your startup, look to work in that industry for
    someone else for a while. Gaining experience and
    knowledge while still earning an income is invaluable.

In the following chapters, I will talk you through what needs
to happen next.

2

YEAR ZERO

Every January, millions of British people make a New Year's resolution to start a business. Remarkably, about 400,000 new businesses are registered every year in the UK, so some of them actually do it.[2] But many try and give up just as quickly, discovering it's not as easy as they'd hoped. In fact, it's far from easy, so only a tiny proportion survive Year One.

Getting Year Zero right and never, ever giving up are the two factors you need to be in that tiny minority.

Year Zero is the year before you change your life forever. This is the planning phase of your new adventure and it might last longer than a year.

---

2   B Shaw, 'Business demography, UK: 2019', Office for National Statistics, 2020, www.ons.gov.uk/businessindustryandtrade/business/activitysizeand location/bulletins/businessdemography/2019

For me, Year Zero actually lasted two years, which were filled with intense planning and serious conversations with trusted contacts. In actual fact, I had been preparing for my startup throughout my entire life as I grew up surrounded by the family business started by my great-great-grandfather in 1888 (more about that later). I've met up with people from my Woolies days who remember me banging on about starting my own business eleven years before I actually did it. I have ideas in laptops that are only extractable by floppy disk. Running my own business is in my blood and the roots are deep. There has never been any question in my mind how much I wanted it.

What is it about your idea that makes you feel like that?

Your Year Zero is all about preparation for your giant leap off the cliff. It's the year that precedes startup and it makes your business idea more real than it has ever been before. The more preparatory work you put in during Year Zero (ideally while you are still being paid by someone else), the greater your chance of success. The planning is a good exercise in itself as you will soon discover how serious you are and reassess how strongly the fire inside you is burning as the months race by.

Setting the date you will start your business will put an end to ambiguity and help everyone around you to see and accept that the big change in your life is for real. Commit to that date now. Write in your diary, calendar, Filofax, phone: 'On *insert date here*, I will start my business'. Pick one year from now. If you're truly hardcore and have kids alongside your business baby, use their growth in that year as a benchmark that perfectly demonstrates how time flies. It's a good introduction to the weirdness of time moving quickly (as you work all hours to get things in place) and slowly (as you're looking forward to the date you will start your business) at the same time.

Then work backwards, month-by-month, putting reminders in your diary: 'Eleven, ten, nine, etc months of employment left'. This will make it real and keep the ticking clock at the front of your mind, so that your dream won't disappear in the diversions of daily life.

> Key learning: You have one short year to get everything in place to determine whether you are going to be successful.

The first decision you need to make is your purpose. At this stage, it can be as simple as knowing what you will call your current role in your future business. Trust me, this is important. You need to know how to describe your purpose right now in the business you are building.

Your purpose

Not all the details of your big idea are likely to be clear yet, but you need an absolutely superclear answer to the question you'll be asked thousands of times: 'What do you do?' When you are a cog in someone else's machine, the answer is on your business card or your lanyard. When you decide to go out on your own and start a business, overnight, it becomes nigh on impossible to say exactly what you do.

You might still be working at your day job during your preparatory Year Zero, but you need to start networking and making contacts, and for that, you'll require a concise way of introducing yourself. When I started out, I found it really tough to succinctly and accurately summarise my amazing attributes. And the problem got bigger every time I met someone new.

You have one chance to make a first impression, so you can't just blurt out a muddled, lengthy speech that ultimately doesn't mean anything. Granted, it's complicated, but if you don't know what your new purpose is, you're never going to impress anyone else with your business idea.

Here are some options I tried out:

- ❖ Managing director – but of what, exactly? At this stage, I wasn't managing anyone or directing anything.
- ❖ Director – a lot of people end up using this option, giving the impression that there are already other directors in their team, which never felt honest enough for me.
- ❖ CEO – not when you're starting out.
- ❖ Founder – maybe. This takes ownership without being too showy.
- ❖ Entrepreneur – no, just no. Never. Unless you already have several successful businesses to your name, 'entrepreneur' reeks of delusions of grandeur.

You can try a mash-up of any of the above (apart from entrepreneur, of course) – founder and CEO, perhaps – but generally, if you use multiple titles, you end up digging yourself into an even deeper hole. Unless you're heavily funded or the next silicon unicorn, I would avoid this.

In the end, I arrived at 'creator', but I kept that to myself, and quite rightly so. It felt like the only word to summarise my goal for the next year: I was creating something special. Something disruptive, shiny and new. A company, but I didn't know exactly what type of company.

For the outside world, I didn't use 'creator'; I said, 'I'm starting a business', and I recommend that to you, too, as you plan your startup, because it's exactly what you are doing. And you can seamlessly move on to the slightly less dull 'I started a business last year' once that milestone passes.

Some people may ask how it's going. Despite all the pain, blood, sweat and tears that you may be going through behind the scenes, your instant response should always be 'Everything's great'. Better still, make sure you have one or two reasons why it is the best thing you've ever done to hand and seize the opportunity to rattle them off. Of course, this will often prompt the other person to wax lyrical about the business they want to start, but don't let that put you off.

'I own a business' or 'I'm a founder of a so-and-so business' will work until you pass Year Three. At this point, most people will assume that you're a millionaire and be mightily impressed by your success, even if it isn't true. Let them be impressed, because starting a business and surviving is really hard.

> Key learning: Know your business purpose, and how you are going to articulate that to the outside world.

Your values

You've clarified your purpose. Now you need to nail the values which will keep you going through the hard times to follow. Before you talk to anyone you want to do business with, establish the values to guide how you will do business.

> Key learning: your values can't just be words; they must be at the centre of everything you do.

One of my early pitches was to a man who described his unique selling point (USP) as 'Being nice and kind'. He said it was such a rare thing in business that it helped him to stand out. It really stuck with me – that man *was* kind, and nice. He believed it and delivered it in every conversation he had.

Being kind isn't a weakness. In fact, I view it as one of my greatest strengths. But after much deliberation, the values I decided on were:

- ❖ Trust
- ❖ Attitude
- ❖ Honesty
- ❖ Ambition

They are widely held, obvious and appealing to most people who hear them.

In the first few months of my Year Zero, I made more than 500 phone calls to anyone who would speak to me about what I wanted to do, and I received a lot of great advice and guidance in return. I also talked to a lot of voicemails, but that's par for the course. I originally had my values laid out as Honesty, Attitude, Trust and Ambition; inadvertently, I had created the rather dull acronym HATA. During one of my phone conversations, a really helpful adviser suggested the fabulous TAHA instead.

'TAHA, I've arrived!' I thought. It felt like a breakthrough. The part of my pitch where I talked about my brand values resonated with people. I had no clients and no work at that stage, but I still had valuable things to say.

Dealing with the naysayers

The preparation you need to put in place in Year Zero is much more in-depth than you may have considered. It requires a lot of time and it becomes more scary as you go on. Fear may feel like it's crippling you as the start date gets closer: the worries, the self-doubt, the mockery, the endless queue of people warning you that what you're proposing is madness. Sadly, my experience was that practically everyone I spoke to told me why I shouldn't do it.

It's your choice who you talk to about your plans, but if you do tell people, keep a list of those who don't immediately shoot them down. Those people will become your guardian angels. Over the years, they will provide the emotional support you need to survive. They will be your allies, both as you progress forward and on the days when it feels like you're only moving backwards.

What of the naysayers? None of them are bad people. Ironically, their negative responses will help you achieve the right mindset to succeed. You might fall out with some of them, but that only indicates the passion you have for what you want to do. And if your reaction to the naysayers' negativity gets stronger over time, then that is only a good thing.

The reality is that they are afraid for you. They don't want you to fail and lose everything you have. If they are close to you, their fear is actually based in love. As human beings, we are inherently designed to remove discomfort from our lives. We feel cold, we put a jumper on; we feel hot, we take the jumper off. Starting a business presents an overwhelming amount of discomfort for you and those who love you.

Make time

Giving yourself at least a year to prepare will go some way towards dispersing the fear as you get closer to your deadline. A year may seem like a long time, and it is, in fact, plenty – if you're committed to working hard on your plans.

Doing your planning while you're earning a regular salary is the ideal scenario. But if you're earning a good salary, your day job is likely to be exhausting and time-consuming. It might not leave a lot of time for you to focus on your new business. You'll be fitting that in after work and at weekends. If you like to watch hours of TV, play computer games, paint watercolours, do up your home, make models or tinker with cars in your free time, the brutal truth is that you will have to give all of that up.

Does the idea of giving up your spare time for twelve months not appeal? You're not alone – only the most driven will be able to commit fully to Year Zero. If you've got a young family, forget it – just wait a few years. If you're in a long-term relationship, then it's going to be extra tough as you need to trade some of your quality couple time to do something on your own. It's incredibly selfish to start a business. Your partner will need patience and understanding (more about this in Chapter 7).

If you have an agreement with your partner that you play golf or tennis at the weekend, or Sunday morning is for car boot sales, or you have regular mini-breaks with your mates, give up all of that. All of it. Allocate every spare moment to planning your business. When you're in Year Zero, and you want your startup to succeed, give up everything and go all the way.

I viewed it as a trade-off. In my last job, my normal working hours were eight to six, plus two hours' daily commute. Once I started my business, I could replace my previous working and commuting hours with a twelve-hour day, meaning I would get my evenings and weekends back.

> **Key learning: I traded my spare time in Year Zero to earn the right to spare time in Year One. And so can you.**

From the start of Year Zero, I have treated my business as my hobby. Some people play with trains in the garage, I play with spreadsheets. I love my business and I'm learning new skills every day. Even now, I (perhaps weirdly) consider time spent working alone on my business plans as 'me time'. It is still my hobby because I enjoy every day, and a lot of starter-uppers feel the same. It's the only way to succeed.

To plan your startup between working full time and enjoying your personal life, you will need discipline. It takes hours in front of a computer on your own, so pick one or two, or a few evenings a week (the more, the better), or sections of the weekend to get down to serious planning, no interruptions. Everyone around you might moan, so it's up to you to decide how much you want this business. And how much you want it will be defined by how much you are prepared to sacrifice.

Get ready to fail

Despite your meticulous planning in Year Zero, little will happen the way you thought it would. Annoying, right? If I look at my Year Zero notes, spreadsheets and plans, barely anything remains as part of the business.

It turned out the most useless things were my forecasting spreadsheets, which is a shame because I love a spreadsheet. I endlessly planned income, turnover, gross profit, net profit and everything else, all colour coded in Excel with VLOOKUPs, charts and summaries. I reviewed and critiqued my work, questioning and dividing totals to make them less unrealistic.

When I look at those spreadsheets now alongside what is actually happening for real, I realise that they're useless for two reasons:

Revenue: whatever you think you will earn on paper, the reality will be a tiny fraction of it, particularly in Year One. Also, you need to plan for the money to take much longer to hit your bank account than you may expect (more on this in Chapter 5).

Costs: even if you've gone through the spreadsheets with a plethora of fine-tooth combs and worked out every penny you'll need to spend, it won't be enough. There will be costs you are simply not aware of yet, and as your business grows, the list will get longer.

All successful businesspeople have failed at some point. And most are happy to share their failures with whoever wants to listen, so you can learn from their experiences. Speaking to the right people about your ideas is invaluable, and it's amazing how many successful businesspeople are willing to give free advice.

Year Zero is your practice run. Fail a lot and fail fast. Evolve and improve your ideas. This is your opportunity to learn and move on; it is how you handle failure that will determine your success.

Most of my Year Zero ideas, processes, models and strategies ended up on the scrapheap, but they were still all valuable. Being a startup is about being flexible, being adaptable, being able to follow and adjust to the market. All markets are constantly changing and my scrapheap ideas have evolved and fed into something else.

This is your time to try things out and test your ideas. Your time to be brave and vulnerable, discussing your ideas with people you know, like, trust and respect.

> Key learning: Every successful businessperson has failed at some point. Failure is your opportunity to learn.

Sharing gets serious

Use Year Zero to reach out to the people you know in business, and to potential clients. This is a massive reality wakeup call that requires a lot of faith in the people you are sharing your idea with, especially if you are still working for someone else. If you speak to someone you could potentially do business with and they say they are interested, what a boost that will be.

This is another reason for setting your startup date in your diary. One of the first questions the people you speak to about your ideas will ask is, 'When are you going to do it?' If you can tell them a specific month, or better still, an actual day of the month, the conversation gets serious. If they can see that you're for real, they will also be more likely to be generous with free advice. If you can't give them a date, the conversation may move on and you'll miss your opportunity.

As your plans become more refined, keep working on your pitch. I created a series of work-in-progress pitching decks to introduce my company to the people I wanted to do business with, running through and rehearsing each one until I knew it by heart. But pitches need to constantly evolve, so ensure that every time you pitch, you make marginal gains to inch yourself forward. As I gratefully chewed the cud with one kind person after another, the value of different parts of my pitch became clearer to me.

Use this time and opportunity as your practice ground. You are working towards an evolving pitch that takes fewer than five minutes to deliver. You also need an elevator pitch, which sums up what you do in a short sentence. The current 'elevator pitch' for my company, The Point.1888, is:

> 'We bring retailers and brands together to create new products and experiences.'

> **Key learning:** Get your elevator pitch ready for a chance meeting with Sir Richard Branson.

I was enjoying the tennis at Wimbledon in 2011 and found myself standing behind Sir Richard in the queue for the gents'. He even let me go in front of him. This was before my Year Zero stage and I missed my elevator pitch opportunity. As I frantically looked round to see where the great man was, I realised that destiny had given me a shot and I'd blown it. I wasn't ready, but you will be.

Financing your venture

Just Survive Somehow has a whole chapter dedicated to money, but a key task in Year Zero is financial planning. Do a full review of your own personal spending budget (and that of your partner if you have joint finances), your monthly bills and all other costs. Work out the minimum you need to survive each month, cutting out everything you can. It's not fun, but it's interesting to see where you are currently throwing your money away. This process also helps to remove one of the biggest startup excuses:

'I don't have the money yet'. People who say they don't have the money often haven't even worked out how much money they need.

If you have a partner who works, that's a big bonus, but don't expect them to be your bank. When you calculate your personal monthly burn rate, include all the household costs and bills if you want to stay in that relationship. I made sure I did this and it worked like a dream as I am still married.

Once you have your monthly burn rate, work out how you can get twelve to eighteen months' worth of cash together so that you can survive without earning. By saving for two years, remortgaging my house and borrowing some money from my grandma (nicknamed Grandma Theft Auto by a 'mate'), I raised enough to survive for eighteen months. Every time I earned some money, I added a week to the end of my personal budget spreadsheet. At that stage, my business was purely about survival, and this backup cash helped to remove the horrendous possibility of not being able to pay the bills.

> Key learning: Plan ahead and save the money to survive financially for a year to eighteen months, even if your business earns nothing.

Year Zero can be as long or as short as you want it to be. It doesn't matter as long as you start your Year One eventually. A word of warning, though: spending too long in Year Zero may result in your idea no longer being relevant. Once you have your finance and burn rate sorted, the good news is that there aren't any further excuses to stop you. It's startup time.

CHEAT SHEET

Let's have a quick look back at what we have covered in this chapter.

✧ Don't call yourself an entrepreneur. Tell everyone you like, trust and respect that you are starting a business. Give them the start date, ideally one year from now.

✧ There will be naysayers when you first share your business idea, probably lots of them. Ironically, their negativity can strengthen your resolve and show how passionate you are about your business idea.

✧ Year Zero is your year of endless failure. Fail a lot and fail fast. How you learn and move on from your failures in Year Zero will be vital to your successes in Year One and beyond.

✧ Put in the hours of preparation and planning while your employer is still paying the bills. If you're going to do it, go all the way. It means giving up a lot of your free time for a year, but it pays off in Year One if you dedicate time now in your diary to focus on your business. It's also good preparation for when you start for real.

- ⟡ Find a purpose – don't do it for the money.

- ⟡ Create a list of brand values – a code that you want to be known for. Live them in every conversation you have. Have them tattooed on your face if you must.

- ⟡ Test and evolve your pitch. Identify what is valuable in your business idea to create a pitch that is polished and special.

- ⟡ All successful businesspeople have valuable experience to share, and many are happy to do so. Make sure you're speaking to the right people.

- ⟡ You never know when you're going to bump into Sir Richard Branson, so have your one-sentence elevator pitch practised, polished and ready to air at any given opportunity.

- ⟡ Scrutinise your finances, get rid of anything that's not essential and work out how you can survive with no income for twelve to eighteen months. This gives you peace of mind that the bills will still be paid during the lean times.

3

WHAT IS THE POINT?

Seriously, what is the point? This is a question to apply to every aspect of your life, but it is even more critical when you're starting a new business. Why do you want to do this, really?

Generally, there are two reasons why people want to start a business:

1. To become rich and famous. Chances of success – tiny.
2. To change the world. Chances of success – slightly more than tiny.

If you choose the second option, you can make it achievable. You just need to be able to define the positive change you want to make. Success is not about the size of the change.

This chapter is all about getting absolutely clear why you're starting a new business, and the unique and appealing brand your 'why' will create. Without a clear and compelling reason, why give everything up that you have worked for? All those late nights clawing your way up the corporate ladder, the lifestyle you enjoy with holidays and nice dinners? Money, of course, is important, but the why behind your business idea should go way beyond financial gain.

Once you've defined your why, the point of your business, everything else will make sense. You'll have something solid to build on and a yardstick to measure against. The why, the point, needs to be the cold, hard reason that will prevent you from giving up when the going gets tough.

It is ultimately your why that will influence your branding. Before we explore the reason behind you starting out on your own, let's have a look at the importance of the brand.

What's in a name?

Remember – you are not starting a business. You are starting a brand.

I love brands and brand names. Of course I do, because I work in an industry that's all about brand identity. Branding is incredibly important for any business.

I always ask business owners that I meet where their brand name came from and the story behind it. I particularly enjoy asking the question when the answer seems obvious. Often, they respond with something unexpected, which provides me with some insight into the person I'm talking to.

Naming your company is one of the joys of starting up. It's a bit like naming your children. You have to do it, and although you can change the name later, that's not ideal. Long before a new business becomes real, most starter-uppers are thinking about their company name and what the logo will look like.

> Key learning: Having a brand identity from the outset that is futureproof, has meaning and looks good is the goal.

By its very nature, a brand or company name will have an interesting story behind it. You'll be telling that story on repeat – when you're starting out, you won't have much else to talk about to prospective clients, and little or no proof that you can deliver – so make sure you do it justice.

As an example, here's the story in two parts of how my business name, The Point.1888, came about.

1: The Point

There are hundreds of 'trial' brand names and logos sitting in my PC archive that I can't bring myself to bin. One day, they might be useful to someone, or maybe not, but none of them really fitted with what I had in my head or gut.

I'd wanted to live in Blackheath since playing rugby there as a teenager. In the summer of 2013, I was at a barbecue, chatting to long-time friends who both now claim that they actually named my company. I was explaining the struggle I was having coming up with a name for my new business that I loved and that carried meaning.

We went through all the places we'd known growing up. Suddenly, my favourite place in London came to mind: Point Hill on the edge of Blackheath. It's a beautiful spot that nobody goes to because it's not on the Tube and is beyond Greenwich, which soaks up all the visitors.

The first time I actually found 'The Point', literally and metaphorically, was in 2005. When I bought my first flat in Lewisham ('Blackheath Borders', as the estate agent called it), another friend, who had grown up in the area, told me about an amazing place with unrivalled views of London that only the local residents know about. I bought a map and, out jogging one Sunday morning, I found it. As I came through the trees, the view took the little breath I had left away. I'd run five miles (those were the days!) and I was bright red and sweating like a racehorse, staggering up the hill and looking over the most amazing view of my home city. I knew I had found 'my place', and it remains my favourite spot in London today.

Decision made. My company was going to be called The Point.

I liked the fact that people would ask me 'What's The Point?' and I could wax lyrical about my business why and how I was going to change the world. But as I imagined inspirational posters for future advertising campaigns, I soon discovered that there were literally hundreds of companies called The Point and all the web addresses and social media handles were already taken. Just The Point wasn't going to be enough.

This is where the family business came in.

2: 1888

My family heritage is extremely important to me. I've often wondered what early years in business were like for my great-great-grandfather, Joseph Thomas Miller (JTM to the family). It all started in 1888, the year the Football League was formed, the game of Snakes and Ladders and the pneumatic tyre were invented, and Jack the Ripper was terrorising the streets of east London. There was no email, no business insurance or liability clauses, no workers' rights and limited technology. There was the telephone, but even if you had one, there was nobody to call as nobody else did. But business, innovation and invention were all thriving. You really could change the world.

My dad often tells the story of how, back in 1888, JTM looked across the road in Borough at the jam factory where workers were unloading sacks of fruit. To protect their work suits, they had stitched the fruit sacks together to make aprons. JTM's lightbulb moment occurred. He crossed the road, met the manager and offered to make aprons and overalls for the workers. There and then, they agreed a working relationship and shook hands on it. Slick. No contracts with indemnity clauses and endless hours of formalising how things would work and the terms of business. Just a simple agreement between two men who saw value in one another.

I often think about the current state of play for formalising client contracts and wonder if it is an improvement on that model. Yes, we can now access the entire world through LinkedIn and acquire clients from anywhere we want to, but is it really better? Local business for local people, built on principles, honesty, trust and respect. I wanted to harness all the positive heritage of my family's good old days and put it at the centre of my modern company.

I've always liked the figure 8. It's cuddly and I like its symmetry. I also have a huge passion for the British & Irish Lions rugby team, who were top of my dream client list in 2014 and signed as a client in 2020. Their branding is unique in such a traditional sport, and they first went on tour in… yes, 1888.

When I started the business, I didn't have the head space to think about the value of 8 in the global marketplace, but I appreciate it now. In Chinese culture, 8 is regarded as the luckiest number and contains meanings of prosperity, success and high social status. Also, it is pronounced *ba* in Chinese, which sounds very similar to the word *fa*, which means to make a fortune. What's not to like?

It is important to stand out from the crowd. I wanted to ensure that both customers and clients would see my business as different from all the other licensing agencies, that it was unique and disruptive. The licensing industry has been around for decades, driven by a desire from consumers to want new ideas and new ways of doing things. As I set out to be different from my more established competitors, the numbers, 1888, helped me to do that. All of my competitors seemed to be known or defined by acronyms. My company was going by numbers, not letters.

The company name was going to be The Point.1888.

Brand names need to be memorable. Try saying The Point eighteen eighty eight out loud. It's not quick or easy. But it is memorable.

Why brands matter

For Generation X-ers like myself, toy and sweet brands are likely to have been the first we were exposed to. Today, my kids have constantly had brands hammered into their subconscious from birth. I've always felt a strong attachment to brands and there are many that made an impact on me as a child and brought forth a lifetime of loyalty – the holy grail for brand marketeers. For me, Yazoo (the drink, not the band) and Monster Munch is still the breakfast of champions.

For teenagers, peer pressure creates a whirlwind of 'must haves'. They'll happily claim they're loyal to one brand, then drop it in a 180-degree about turn when it's no longer cool. Teenagers swarm around brands until everyone has the same trainers. In some ways, it's like a disease, continually infecting each other with the message that 'you'll be cool' or 'you'll fit in'. Nail those two, and every kid will want to buy your product.

> Key learning: Your brand – the words, the logo, the strapline, the typeface, the design, the colours, the background – is critical to your success.

Brands and brand identity are more important than ever before because everyone can now access the global market. Brands surround us all the time. Most of us are exposed to 4,000 to 10,000 every single day, so how is it that some of them go into our brain and grab us? And more importantly – how do they stay front of mind? There's no definitive answer to these questions, but an authentic why and a compelling story behind your brand that truly reflect who you and your business are is the best place to start.

Do I still eat pickled onion Monster Munch because of the taste? The nostalgia? The price? The logo? The funny monster shape? I just don't know, but I've been loyal to that brand for over thirty-five years, and I would be gutted if it disappeared.

Brand marketing is clever and complicated. In fact, to me, it's pure genius. I am fascinated by the intangible values of brands. Granted, not everyone is as weird as me.

To test out my theories, I decided to find out whether what I was doing in my business made sense to kids of today. In 2018, I spent a day at the Arthur Terry School Careers Fair in Birmingham – 1,750 twelve- to eighteen-year-olds flowing through the doors, 150 at a time. I had left school twenty years earlier, and I soon realised how out of touch I was.

My initial technique of rattling off my favourite words – 'brand extension', 'revenue', 'budgets', 'profit', 'licensing' – failed badly, unsurprisingly. The guy next to me had a £1,500 drone, which he was taking out to the playground for test flights; the RAF stand opposite had four of those pull-up banner-type things; there were lawyers, universities, apprentice schemes, and even a guy selling 'become a professional footballer' academy courses. All were more appealing than the fancy new brand postcards I had laid out.

I realised that I had been woefully underprepared and hugely outgunned. For the previous four years, around 95% of my conversations had been about my company and why it was so special. But this wasn't going to wash because nobody here knew what brand licensing was, so how on earth was I going to get the kids' attention, let alone keep them interested?

I decided the way forward was to ask two key questions:

1. If I offered you a Coke or a Pepsi, which would you choose, and why? Oh, how I wished I had prepared and brought props. As expected, only one kid said Pepsi. That's less than 0.1%.

2. What's your favourite brand / shop / clothing / food, and why? More than 80% of the boys said Nike.

Both questions encouraged the students to consider what a brand is.

Your why – purpose

Now we come on to the all-important reason behind your business. The why of a business, as outlined in Simon Sinek's excellent *Start With Why*,[3] splits into two key parts:

1. The purpose of your business
2. The brand values you'll follow to deliver that purpose

Today, to stand out and scale up, be disruptive and unique, attract business through reputation and recommendation, and make a dent in your marketplace, you must first have your brand purpose and values nailed. Many of the people who will be your

---

3   S Sinek, *Start With Why: How great leaders inspire everyone to take action* (Penguin, 2011)

customers and clients care about purpose and values, so you must, too.

> Key learning: You need to start thinking about purpose and values in Year Zero. It's the first step in any business plan.

The success of The Point.1888 is largely due to the fact that in 2014, I had the purpose and values clearly established; they formed the backbone of my company charter. The legendary team I have hired obviously makes the biggest impact, but other than my brand, the only things that haven't changed since I started the company are the purpose and values.

The Point.1888's purpose is simple:

1. Change the world through giving 11% of company profits to charity
2. Provide staff with a true life-work balance through offering ultra-flexibility

Charity

My team and I are all incredibly lucky to have the jobs we do and live in the world we live in. Giving back and being a socially progressive company are important to all of us. Hearing on the local news that an Essex Air Ambulance landed on the M11 and saved someone's life, and knowing that our support means the rescue service can continue, makes what we do purposeful.

When your startup grows and becomes more successful, you can make an impact and change lives. By supporting those less fortunate, you gain a purpose more important than just making money. According to a recent study by Girls With Impact,[4] 45% of Gen-Zedders want to work for a company that makes a positive difference in the world. Today, it's one of the most important factors in attracting talented people to come to work for you. At The Point.1888, my team only recruits people that share our purpose.

Imagine if every company committed to giving 11% of its profits to charity. Imagine if every banker gave 11% of their Christmas bonus to charity, think about the difference that could make. It's worth so much more than just buying another watch or dress.

We all pay tax, and most of us complain about it. Commit early in your business plan to being socially progressive, too. The satisfaction, joy and pleasure are great.

Ultra-flexibility

The second part of The Point.1888's purpose is to give team members – or rather, the honest, dedicated and talented individuals who join my rollercoaster – fully flexible working. That's any hours, any day and anywhere. It's not important to me where people work or what time of day they are most effective; what is important to me is trust, and I trust them to get the

---

4   M Perna, 'Gen Z wants to change the world – at your company', *Forbes*, 2019, www.forbes.com/sites/markcperna/2019/12/10/gen-z-wants-to-change-the-world-at-your-company/?sh=3043a1703c56

job done on their terms. This philosophy is built on responsibility, task and communication. I assume everyone that I employ will act responsibly with the power they have, and I trust them to deliver.

I find it appalling that mainstream employment seems to regard parents, particularly mothers, as unemployable because they might want a slightly different set-up in their working hours. Since I became a father myself, I have gained so much respect for any parent who even attempts to hold down a job.

When you become a parent, life changes. Everything you knew before is turned upside down, including your emotions. Having work that fits around your life is a game changer. More and more businesses are offering this, but the uptake from many companies seems painfully slow.

I see this as an opportunity – The Point.1888 gets access to phenomenal talent purely on a technicality. I employ a lot of parents in part-time roles and let people work around their personal circumstances. What they give back is awesome in terms of commitment, dedication and loyalty – things that a massive salary cannot necessarily command.

What's your first action? Nail your purpose. Call it vision, mission, goals or whatever, but make sure you are clear on your why.

Key learning: If there's no why, then why bother? What is the point?

Your why – brand values

The next step – maybe something for day two of your Year Zero – is to get your brand values nailed. As we saw in Chapter 2, they tell the external world how you will conduct your business, what it will be like to work with you and what you and your business stand for.

Many corporations have brand values that they've paid an agency to invent to make themselves feel better. The reality is big companies often struggle with change. If a corporate's new brand value is going to be 'collaborative' when it's operated for twenty years with 'ruthless', it's unlikely to embrace it overnight.

The Point.1888's brand values have been tweaked slightly since inception. Now, they are:

- ✥ Family
- ✥ Attitude
- ✥ Ambition and bravery
- ✥ Trust

And what lovely words they are, too. I'm sure many companies have shiny, fluffy directional words stacked into an infographic on their website or plastered on coffee cups, but brand values are a complete waste of time unless they become central to everything the company does. If purpose is the brain, brand values are the blood.

The problem with values is that they may be set internally, but they need to be validated externally by everyone you do business with. Constantly. You have to show that you believe in your brand values in every interaction your business makes; every conversation your team has; every meeting you go to. Over time, people will start to recognise these values as reflecting who you and your business are and what you can offer to the world, so make sure you choose ones that are truly authentic.

> Key learning: Make sure you and everyone within your business live and breathe by your values.

The growth of The Point.1888 and the amount of new business it attracts are, I believe, directly down to the companies that we've worked with recognising my team and I to be who we say we are. The best new business you can get is from an external client or customer recommending you to someone they know. Think about the level of trust, respect and love that takes – it can be a game changer.

Write a Dream Ambition statement that wraps up your purpose and values – your why – in your ultimate vision. Setting your endgame at the beginning will be hugely valuable for growth and success. In the first few weeks of starting up, I wrote a Dream Ambition statement: a five-year vision that detailed everything I hoped I would achieve in that time. Writing my first book was the last thing I needed to tick off the list – TICK!

CHEAT SHEET

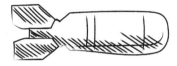

In this chapter, we have had a good look at branding and the all-important why behind your business, covering:

✧ What the point of your startup idea is. Its why has to be compelling.

✧ Deciding on your brand name – make it clever and memorable.

✧ Nailing a purpose. Make it meaningful with a positive effect on the world, and then stick to it. Shout it from the rooftops – be known for this purpose more than anything else.

✧ Looking at your own morals and ethics. Define how you want people to feel when they do business with you. Make sure you can live and die by your brand values.

✧ Going back to school and speaking to teenagers about branding. I guarantee you will learn something.

4

CHOOSING AND PITCHING YOUR BUSINESS'S 'WHAT'

In Year Zero, you set a start date in your diary and worked on your survival fund. You nailed your purpose and beautiful brand values. It's all coming together nicely. But there is another question that we have so far overlooked: what is your company actually going to do? What problem is it going to solve?

Most starter-uppers will know exactly what their business is going to do as they tend to come up with the what before the why, how and when. Anyone can set up a business to do something, but the only way clients are going to pay you to do your thing is if you can prove they have a problem that you, and only you, can solve for them.

One of the joys of having the freedom to beep your own horn is that you can follow the market, adapt your model and be agile when your competitors can't. The company you think you are starting now may become something different over time as the demands of the market evolve.

I wasn't entirely sure what my company was going to do. I knew who my ideal clients would be (people who shared the same values as me) and the problem my company would solve, but the bits of the puzzle didn't come together exactly as I planned. You can only truly identify and lock down the problem your target audience has and your solution to that problem when you have pitched the idea probably 100 times, following Dave Brailsford's principle of marginal gains (getting 1% better every day).[5] If you're not following this principle and your competitors are, you will soon become obsolete.

Choosing your industry

Ideally, you already work in the industry that you intend to start up in. Base a huge part of your research into creating your purpose and values on your target industry. Your purpose and values are the bedrock of your USP, so formulate them as part of the research you are doing on your target market.

If you don't already work in the industry in which you want to start a business, I urge you to go and do so for at least a year, ideally more. I love it when solicitors become artisan bread makers and bankers become electric car makers, even though it astounds me that any of them are successful. Whenever you hear in the

---

5   R Moore, *Mastermind: How Dave Brailsford reinvented the wheel* (BackPage Press, 2013)

news about an apparently miraculous 'overnight success', you can be sure that it actually comes on the back of months and probably years of hard work and dedication to gain the all-important experience we all need.

It's unlikely that you have more money than sense, and even less likely that you will have identified something in the iced-coffee market that hundreds of thousands of industry professionals have missed. That's not to say it won't happen, but your best chance of success is to launch a better or modified version of whatever your last employer produced. The advantages are huge – you will have several years' experience in the actual industry, you'll have a network within it and you'll have a bundle of cred-ibility, putting you ahead of any outsider. Nobody appreciates an outsider seagulling in and telling an expert what they have been missing for decades – just watch *The Apprentice* or *Dragons' Den* if you don't believe me.

At this stage, you either have a dream that you will one day run the best iced-coffee company in the world, or you have a strategy that enables you to improve on something that already exists. It's not the first to market who normally wins; it's the most adaptable of the second phasers who tends to take home the prize. Innocent smoothies are a perfect example. PJ Smoothies launched as first to market and nobody's heard of them today.

If you are in the dreamers' group, go and learn the ropes in the iced-coffee industry, or whichever industry you dream about. You might have it all wrong and your dream is just that: a dream. On the other hand, you could find the clarity you need about what will set you apart to push you off the startup cliff.

> Key learning: Gain experience in the industry you want your business to operate in, ideally while you're still earning money.

Barriers to entry

The first thing to consider when building your business plan is how difficult it will be to start up (and how many people just like you that you will have to deal with). This is a vital part of Porter's Five Forces,[6] the model used to analyse competition. I urge you to read up on this to give you a great insight into the pain ahead of you. Forewarned is forearmed.

When I decided to start a business, I had two main options: retail and marketing services agency. I'd worked in various roles in shops for seventeen years of my professional life. In my Woolies days, I'd thought about opening a shop and building it into a chain, which is something loads of people did back then.

If you're constantly selling products to customers, you have a low risk from a cash flow point of view. But when you consider the reality of opening any kind of shop, the barriers to entry have always been extreme, even without the huge hit retail has taken since 2020 and the Covid pandemic. To rent a physical space to sell from, you will need a three-month deposit, which immediately places you in debt every month for potentially the next five years. You then need to invest a lot of cash into something you can sell.

---

6   M Porter, 'The five competitive forces that shape strategy', *Harvard Business Review*, 2008, https://hbr.org/2008/01/the-five-competitive-forces-that-shape-strategy

Retail is responsible for many gravestones labelled 'deceased due to stock issues', so how much stock should you buy? Let's say shelf fill and two weeks' cover (depending on supplier terms). That's going to set you back a tidy sum, and you haven't even sold anything yet. And what have you based your two weeks' cover projection on? Your chances of getting a forecast accurate for a brand-new shop is zero. You can always guess, but you have to choose to go too high or too low. You can never get it spot on.

What about staff for your shop? Maybe you'll staff it yourself and work eighteen hours a day. That doesn't sound like much of a life-work balance, so the answer is to hire at least one other person. Maybe you have a child of working age who you can employ on minimum wages, but if not, there goes more money. And you still haven't sold anything yet.

Then there are the utilities to consider. If you sign up to, say, twelve-month terms for electricity, heating, broadband, phones, etc, that's more money out the door. And you *still* haven't... I'm sure you get the picture.

But wait, then there's the shop fit. Hopefully, you will move into a site that is perfect for your business, but it's more than likely it won't be. In the exciting startup phase, you'll probably be tempted to go all out on fixtures and fittings – not everybody likes the charity shop vibe – so you could suddenly be tens of thousands of pounds down before you've even started.

This is terrifying. Your survival fund, once you work out your monthly costs, is going to need to be around £100,000 just for six months. Cash flow is the most common reason that so many startups fail.

In contrast, starting a marketing services agency requires you to buy a laptop, get an internet connection (the one you already have at home will suffice) and a phone (also already in place). And that's pretty much it.

You will need a brilliant network and fantastic relationships with key people within your industry, or at least make sure your why is so compelling that when people meet you, they are drawn into working with you or helping you. To help with this, you will need a clear purpose that you can articulate, convincing the people you meet why you can solve the problem that your target customer has. But your upfront investment is literally the cost of a laptop.

While a marketing services agency may seem a less tangible startup than a retail business, the barriers to entry argument soon swayed me in favour of licensing. Of course, if it's easy for you to enter an industry with your startup, it's also easy for the competition, so you have to set yourself apart.

> Key learning: Be sure to look at the barriers to entry when choosing your industry.

By identifying the barriers to entry for any market, you will be able to truly understand your chances of success in the short term. Remember, Year One in business is all about survival. Survival is success. *Just Survive Somehow.*

Decisions, decisions

Making decisions efficiently is a good habit to get into in Year One. It will stand you in good stead as your business takes off. Procrastinating for too long over any decision, even big ones like what your company is actually going to do, can soon lead to your business idea becoming obsolete.

I spent a lot of time working for huge companies that had a million decision-making gateways to be delicately prised open. It was so frustrating. Remember, making no decision is worse than making the wrong decision.

A wrong decision can quickly become 'the' decision, so you need to focus on turning it into the right one. This isn't always possible, of course; sometimes it's obvious that your first choice is simply not going to work. If that's the case, fail and fail quickly so you can make a new decision and move forward.

> Key learning: Every wrong decision you make will teach you more memorable lessons than the right ones.

Get pitching

You've chosen your industry, so now it's time to get out there and tell the world how amazing you and your fledging sidekick of a company are. This is when you reach for the elegant pitching deck you started in Year Zero and have been perfecting ever since.

Always start with the problem that your prospective client has and explain why you can solve it for them. Don't use the pitch for aggressive selling; rather, explain the benefits of your product in a clear and concise way, and let the client realise the value you can bring.

I apply the marginal gains principle in every aspect of my business. It's my ultimate commitment to embracing change. Everything you do in business, particularly in the startup environment, can be improved. Everything. You only need a marginal improvement each day because over time, these improvements add up.

Starting a company in any industry is competitive. Once you've been successful for several years, it's easy to get lazy and not have a constant improvement process in place. Meanwhile the market – your clients, your competitors and your customers – is moving constantly. Their demands, wants and needs are always evolving. Even when you're still finding your feet, you must adapt your model.

Your pitch document is a key area for marginal gains. It should succinctly summarise everything that is amazing about your idea / concept / company, deliverable inside five minutes. Spend a long time on your pitch documents while you can. Think about who you are pitching to and what might appeal to them. Pictures do tell 1,000 words, so use them wisely.

The Point.1888's pitch document has been updated at least monthly for more than five years. In the first year, it was probably tweaked nearly every week. Every pitch you do gives you an opportunity to change something, reword something, reorder something. Anyone who misunderstands the point you are making is giving you an opportunity for a marginal gain, highlighting that you need to explain or demonstrate something in a better way. As the quote often attributed to Albert Einstein goes, 'If you can't explain it simply, you don't understand it well enough.'

You also need a thirty-second 'elevator pitch'. That's thirty seconds to make an impact, explain who you are and why you are credible, and leave the person you're speaking to wanting to hear more. Learn the latest refined version of this pitch off by heart and have it ready for a chance meeting with Sir Richard Branson, or whoever your hero in business is.

When you first start pitching your business, you have nothing: no clients, no team, no proof and no right to take even five minutes of a busy person's time. In short, you have no right to exist. Learn to accept that you are basically begging for work: all that freedom you dreamed of, and now you have to beg someone to pay you for what you do. This can be humiliating, but it's good groundwork for your business and it's character building. It tests how much you want something, how passionate you are about it and how much belief you have that you can actually make a positive impact.

Key learning: When pitching, you need to be resilient.

You will pitch your business 1,000 times in your first year at the helm. Every time you do it, your chances of success increase because (back to this chapter's favourite topic) you are applying the principle of marginal gains. Resilience is the most important skill you can have as a starter-upper, and it only grows through adversity. How many hits can you take and keep moving forward?

All you need now is the money.

CHEAT SHEET

Again, we have covered a lot in this chapter. To summarise:

✥   Decide what problem you are going to solve for
    your target customer and position yourself as the
    only person who can deliver the solution.

✥   Create a pitch deck that summarises everything that
    is amazing about you in under five minutes.

✥   Apply the principal of marginal gains in everything
    you do.

✥   Work out the barriers to entry for your chosen industry.
    Apply these to your survival fund to ensure you don't run
    out of money.

✥   Be prepared to beg. Be resilient, learn to love the
    begging process and the opportunity that constructive
    feedback brings.

LACK OF CASH
KILLS BUSINESSES.

LACK OF PROFIT

DOES NOT.

5

MONEY, MONEY, MONEY

You have a great idea in a thriving industry and are ready to pitch it at any given moment. You've formulated your mission, purpose and values, and you are close to having learned all you can from doing a job in your chosen industry. But how are you going to finance your venture?

The first question to answer is: how much money do you need? Your Year Zero must not end until you have at least eighteen months' worth of survival cash in the bank.

Despite what ABBA told us, money isn't funny, not even in a rich man's world. Money is the one thing you have to be deadly serious about. The journey you are embarking on will leave you exposed if you do not realise that cash will be central to everything you'll do in Year One.

Lack of profit does not kill businesses; lack of cash does. A study by an American bank revealed that 82% of business failures are due to a lack of cash flow.[7] If you have a cash nest egg for Year One, then you will survive it. Simple as that. You may not build a profitable business in Year One – it would be a rare thing if you did – but you *will* survive it as long as you don't run out of cash. You then have a chance at building a profitable business in Year Two and beyond.

Cash is king

Even before Covid decreed that cash was deadly, it had become almost redundant in our day-to-day lives. Paying with a beep was becoming so ubiquitous that queues at cashpoints had started to look quaint. But despite the fact that few people carry much cash now, if you do so, it can help you achieve an abundance mindset. I still remember holding £25,000 in used banknotes in my first retail job and the feeling of wealth it gave me.

Carry £100 to £200 in cash if you can; get it out of the bank in fivers and tenners. It will make you feel rich even when you are not and it allows you to be generous, a quality you need in abundance in Year One. Be generous with everyone you meet during this time. You will be going for a lot of coffees, often several times a day, and effectively buying somebody's time, so it makes sense to buy their coffee, too. Don't get caught out if the card machine is having an off day. In most cases, if they have given up their time for you, they will already believe in you and therefore will likely offer to pay. When the technology

7   M Flint, 'Cash flow: the reason 82% of small businesses fail', Preferred CFO, 2020, www.preferredcfo.com/cash-flow-reason-small-businesses-fail

is broken and you can't pay by card, if you have old-school cash, you can ride in on your hero's horse to save the day.

> Key learning: Carry cash and offer to buy the coffees, always. Be that hero. Pay £4 for an hour of someone's time. Bargain!

Time is money

This is the number-one lesson I took from Year One. Your true currency is not money, but time. Yes, money gives you options in life, but you – and all the people you meet – are on this planet for such a short period, your time is invaluable.

> Key learning: Trade money for time, not the other way around.

I lived this approach right from Day One. If I could spend money to get time back in my diary, that was a good investment. If I saved money by using my time to do something myself, that stank of failure.

You can apply this to your day-to-day life, too. Do you paint the spare room yourself or pay an expert to do it? The former is trading your time to save money, the latter is trading your money for time.

Thinking time

When you work full time or have a lot of responsibilities, you're likely to have no thinking time. Thinking time (you could call it reading time or learning time) is the key to making your venture not just a reality, but also a success. You can never stop learning about yourself.

A lot of successful people manage their diaries religiously to protect their learning time. *Business Insider* revealed that Warren Buffett spends 80% of his week in the learning/thinking zone.[8] I aim to spend three hours a week in the zone, but I've been looking to increase this.

Give yourself the luxury of thinking time every day. If you have developed a notebook habit as I described in the Introduction – and I urge you to do so – you can make writing your notes part of your thinking time. Review the big things that have happened at the end of each day and read back through your notes from last week, last month and so on to remind yourself of how far you've come.

If you fill every second with 'doing', then your new venture is just going to be one long treadmill. But if you have your survival fund mapped out correctly, getting into the habit of trading money for time and making sure you reflect on and learn from every day will be easy. Without a nest egg, it will be a struggle.

---

8   S Parrish, 'The Buffett formula: Going to bed smarter than when you woke up', Farnham Street blog, 2013, https://fs.blog/2013/05/the-buffett-formula

Investment fund

I called it my survival fund, but an investment fund is a more formal description of your nest egg. It's the money you are prepared to invest in yourself to ensure you can start your business without the immediate issue of cash flow. Your investment fund will become the starting point of the entire financial plan for your business. It's your safety net. Raising your investment fund in Year Zero will alleviate one of the biggest barriers to finally starting up: lack of cash.

If you have worked out your burn rate and how much time you are going to buy for yourself (eighteen months in my case), you will have all you require to work out how big your investment fund needs to be. Open an Excel spreadsheet. This spreadsheet is going to be your best friend. Write your investment fund total in cell A1, and then meticulously log every piece of expenditure you expect to make in the timescale you have given yourself so you can see how your fund will be depleted over time.

You need to be on this spreadsheet every day in Year One. I called mine the 'Cash Bible', and in fact I used it religiously well into Year Three. Split your investment fund into monthly chunks, and instantly you have a forecast-against-budget tracker document. This is the right level of detail to go into at this stage, because everything else is generally unknown. I had a formula that would spit out my projected bankruptcy date based on each item of expenditure I input. It was highlighted in red as a continual warning of the fragility of what I was embarking on.

Once you have forecasted your burn rate, account for all the various set-up costs and additional expenditures that will chip away at your nest egg. There will be costs you hadn't predicted, costs you hadn't expected (including lots of coffees), but you will soon be mini-high-fiving yourself when you can get to a meeting on an off-peak train and save yourself £10. Focus on the pennies as they really do add up. Track everything, including your performance against budget, weekly at least, daily if you can.

At the start, it's likely you won't be spending a lot on travel and food because you will be working at home in a tracksuit. Make sure you're not spending money on clothes, overpriced sandwiches or plastic bottles of water. Giving up my Starbucks habit saved me over £70 per month (£840 per year, or eleven days of survival).

The upside of knowing your bankruptcy date and tracking against it is that you can add payments received on to the same spreadsheet. When I earned a bit of consultancy money in the first couple of months, I worked out that I'd bought myself an extra twenty-six days of survival in business. I knew I could last until March 2016 rather than February 2016. This may seem small, but it's actually huge. This technique of tracking against survival breeds a really good habit for when your business grows.

Key learning: Focus purely on the cash you have and the time that buys you; everything else is a distraction.

Raising your investment

If you're going to be good at this startup thing, you need to be able to raise money. I raised £42,000 at a burn rate of £2,300 per month, meaning I could survive eighteen months before either facing bankruptcy or needing to borrow, and I did this in several ways:

⬥ **Saving.** I saved religiously for two years, which left me with a grand total I was proud of. Saving is hard if you have a life, but it's a good discipline.

⬥ **Remortgaging my house.** If you have an asset such as a house and agreement from any co-owners, such as your partner, it's a great way to raise money. I doubled my survival fund by remortgaging. If you want to do this, you will need to start the process a full six months before you quit your job, otherwise banks will not lend to you. Once you lose your salary, you are considered high risk and the funding opportunity will be gone.

⬥ **Raising external investment.** If you know anybody who has money, ideally a family member or someone who loves you, go and talk to them. Pitch to them and convince them to back you – it's a great test of your pitching ability. I was lucky that my grandma was prepared to listen to my pitch. I showed her what I had raised on my own and she agreed to match my funds, an incredible gift from this incredible woman who changed my life, and potentially those of thousands of others. I will be forever grateful to her, and her legacy will live on through my business.

For the sake of your own mental health, a good survival fund is crucial. I didn't want to borrow from banks or other lenders – you can't start the most amazing adventure of your life and immediately be worrying about the wolves at the door. My dad's advice never to lend or borrow money rings through my ears every day. I wanted a self-funded no-debt business, just as he had achieved before me.

Don't borrow money if you can avoid it. Don't give away equity if you don't have to. One of the joys of running your own business is the freedom of not having to answer to anyone. Don't give away your freedom by getting into debt.

Accountants

Accountants will help you look after your cash. Ideally, get yourself one you know, like, trust and respect, or one recommended by someone you know, like, trust and respect, as soon as possible. I didn't know any accountants, so I searched through local startup forums and chat groups. Starting a business without an accountant is like running an engine without oil. It will run for a while on fumes, but is likely to break at the most inappropriate moment.

Choose your accountant wisely. Invest as much time as possible in meeting with accountants and understanding exactly what they are going to do for you, and how. For example, ask how long you are tied in to your contract in case you want to move. Monthly payment plans may seem good value, but they can have hidden commitments. Speak to founders of other startups to find out what questions they asked. Then speak to their accountants, if they are good.

For once in your life, do read the small print. Most high-street accountants have over fifteen pages of small print, but I urge you to check how long an apparently cost-saving monthly direct debit ties you to the firm. Check what the trigger rates are, based on your success. Mine was based on turnover levels, and they were tight. The more successful I was, the more money the accountant charged.

I still hate the tax, regulation and reporting side of the business. I had to do it all myself for the first few years of my company because the accountant charged me every time I asked a question, but a good accountant is a game changer. A good accountant allows you to trade your money for time. They do all the horrible work and you get to invest more time back into strategic planning, learning or thinking.

Key learning: Your accountant should be working for you, finding every way possible to make your life easier and give you more time to create a successful business.

Tax

When you are in full-time employment, your PAYE deductions may sometimes have come as a shock, but the cold hard truth is that you only truly learn about tax and its impact when you start a business. What a horrible, complicated mess the tax system is. There's a reason big companies have huge accounting teams. I long for the day it can be completely run by artificial intelligence (AI). What a dream that would be for the creative humans on the planet.

I'm sure you want to create amazing things, not spend hours calculating every spend in your business so that you don't cheat the system and get horrible red-stamped brown envelopes sent to your house. But ignore the taxman at your peril.

When you run a startup company, you have limited knowledge and learn on the job. Get the right experts around you to minimise the pain.

VAT

Setting up a private limited company in the UK costs you just £12. It's a bargain. One of the big early decisions you have to make is whether you want to be Value Added Tax (VAT) registered.

VAT is a classic tax that most of us have wilfully ignored most of our lives. The government has decided that we are only adding value to the economy if we are turning over £85,000 or more per year. I didn't register for VAT at the start of my business, despite having ridiculously large forecasts. This was a mistake, as one of my first invoices was from a VAT-registered company. This required me to go back, cap in hand, to my client, explaining that my fee was 20% higher than I had previously quoted. This was an important client and an embarrassing lesson. Check if your suppliers are VAT registered and adjust your quotes accordingly.

I cannot legally give tax advice, but I do believe that being VAT registered shows your ambition. You get a VAT number that you can put on invoices, making your business seem bigger than it possibly is. Bigger customers are likely to respect you for this. More importantly, being VAT registered means you can claim back vast sums from the endless coffees you consume (and the odd notebook and pen).

This is rather embarrassing to admit, but if it helps one person avoid my error, then that makes it worthwhile. Once I was VAT registered, I knew I could add 20% to all of my invoices, so I assumed my turnover had increased 20%. I'm an idiot, but that's what I thought, so I learned this the hard way: ignore VAT on all reporting.

> Key learning: VAT is likely to be the first tax you need to get your head around, particularly in the early years.

Other taxes

There are a lot of taxes. Once you start employing people, you will be paying national insurance contributions, and if you pay yourself a salary, you will pay national insurance and income tax or take dividends where you pay a dividend tax (making you a tiny amount better off). You may one day pay corporation tax on any profits you make, but this is unlikely in Year One. But my 'favourite' tax was one added to my business insurance. You won't need business insurance in the early days, but when you do – hey presto, another tax.

One thing to note – if you get anything wrong with tax, Her Majesty's Revenues and Customs (HMRC) will find you and fine you. No question. It's a fine every time, and some of them are terrifying as they are calculated as a percentage of what you owe. I did appeal to the human nature of the brown-enveloped letter senders from time to time, and they will allow you one or two errors if you speak to them as nicely as you possibly can. But they don't like repeat offenders.

Personally, I think all tax errors you make in Year One should be allowable as an opportunity to educate yourself. Why should you and I be assumed to be dishonest when clearly, we are just unused to an overly complicated tax system.

When clients don't pay

I soon discovered that big companies have the deepest pockets and the shortest arms. They knew that they didn't need to pay me and I'd do the work anyway. And I did.

When I started my company, I thought the hardest part would be to convince clients to pay me for the value I offered. I was so naïve. Everyone who starts a company is naïve. The only people who truly understand how it works are those who have done it before.

If your business is providing services, you don't have anything physical to sell, so you are effectively selling your ideas. In my case, I was selling a concept so alien to a client, I may as well have had 'naïve' written on my forehead. It's not easy to sell services. It takes a lot of convincing, especially at the start when you have no money, no team, no clients and no credibility.

Amazingly, though, I discovered that selling my services wasn't the hardest part. That was actually getting paid.

I'd done all the hard work and, like most starter-uppers, I was getting paid on delivery, not a share up front. I hastily typed out my invoice on headed paper and whizzed it over to the client, expecting to be paid on my 'demanding but fair' thirty days terms. Everything seemed to be in order and I got back to running my business.

Thirty days is a short time in the startup world and the month soon passed. But no payment was forthcoming, so I embarked on the painful payment paper trail.

'I've not been paid. Strange, surely the client company has a system designed to process payments and a moral duty to pay someone what has already been agreed. I'll chase them,' I decided. 'Email is a good idea – quick, easy, efficient and a nice paper trail. Everyone loves receiving emails, particularly ones chasing payments.'

Still no payment.

'I'll call them.'

Voicemail.

'I'll email them again, saying I left a voicemail.'

Wow. Still no payment.

'This doesn't seem to be working!'

I was so naïve.

I had been fantasising about monthly pay cheques, but the reality of running a small business was now smacking me in the face with a shovel. There will be clients who don't pay you. Certainly not on time. And not without several rounds of chasing.

Do you prioritise chasing invoices over generating new business? Another dilemma of the startup world. This stuff is hard. And just when I thought it couldn't get any worse, HMRC decided to wade in at this point and take its share in VAT. Eh? Take the VAT on an invoice that hasn't yet been paid? That doesn't seem right.

But it is.

Big companies are the worst. The bigger they are, the worse they are. They do it because they can. I've had invoices paid a disgraceful five months late. That's the reality you must deal with every day. If you don't have a good investment fund behind you, late payments will kill your cash flow and ultimately your business.

Unfortunately, when clients decide to pay you isn't something you can completely control. I have massively improved at chasing payments over the years; hopefully you will learn how to be a 'squeaky wheel' much more quickly than I did.

You need to be on top of your invoicing process. It's a sad fact that when you start out in business, you're a nobody, a piece of plankton, and you have to use every trick you can think of simply to get paid what you are owed. Forget your morals, ethics and pride. Beg or plead if you have to; appeal to the hearts of invoice accountants, explaining that you're running a small company and you need the money to survive.

Eventually, I changed my payment terms to payment on receipt. It didn't help much, but it meant I could start chasing two days after I'd submitted the invoice. Forget email. When it comes to getting paid for work you've already delivered, get on the phone and start dialling.

> Key learning: Be prepared for money from clients to take a long time to reach your bank account.

You're going to need a bigger boat

You will almost certainly need more money to survive Year One than you think. It's annoying, but it's true. If you have enough money to survive eighteen months, that will likely cover you for the first year.

> Key learning: At the moment, surviving your first year is your only job.

I still know exactly what my survival date is: the date my company would go bankrupt if I earned nothing more from today. It's still based on the concept of money in the bank vs burn rate. I used this concept to start the business, but I have stuck with it ever since, and I advise you to do the same. It's one of my personal key performance indicators (KPIs) and highlights that everything is at risk, a visceral concept that constantly reminds me of the fragility of my dream.

CHEAT SHEET

This may have been a somewhat painful chapter – money can often be a touchy subject – but everything you have learned here will go a long way to making sure you survive Year One. And at this stage of your business, that is all you need to do.

Here's a quick recap:

❖ Lack of cash kills businesses – lack of profit does not. Make sure you have cash in the business from the start.

❖ Work out your survival date by tracking your burn rate against cash in the bank. Keep this date where you can see it as a visual reminder of the fragility of your project.

❖ Time is money. Live by the concept that your only true currency is time. Trade money for time, not the other way around.

   ❖ Find an accountant that you know, like, trust and respect who will genuinely work for you.

   ❖ Don't mess with HMRC – its rules are the only ones you can't break.

❖   You will almost certainly need more money than
     you think. Raise as much as possible in Year Zero
     and keep your costs down. A daily Starbucks is *not*
     an essential expenditure!

❖   Become the best squeaky wheel on the planet –
     get serious about invoices and getting them paid.
     Be on it at all times as you will be at the bottom of
     the priority list for everyone you are billing.

6

IT'S ALL ABOUT THE PEOPLE, PEOPLE!

The whole journey of your business relies on people. Year One is still mainly about you, your circumstances and your environment. Are you the right person to do this? Do you attract the right people? Are you a good judge of character? What does your gut tell you about people? Listen to your gut more than any other organ in business life.

As you move forward, you need to become obsessed with other people and how you interact with them. Your people skills will be truly tested when you start building a team. You are not likely to be recruiting in Year One – paying a salary is a cost that you're probably not ready for yet – but it's a good time to start thinking about the sort of people you want to recruit.

Key learning: Get your people skills right now and they will carry you through.

The thought of actually recruiting during Year One can be terrifying. Choosing that first someone to join you on your journey is a bigger decision than the one to start the business in the first place. But it's the only one that's bigger.

It's important that you have your purpose and values nailed as you think about the culture you want to build and the types of people that the culture may appeal to. You may want to work through the boss list you created in Chapter 1, documenting all the good (and bad) input you've had from your bosses. Think about what type of boss you want to be. There's nobody telling you how you should be any more. It's your choice.

I wanted to be the best boss anyone has ever had. I wanted to provide the perfect job for people. I was also going to be the type of honest boss who says the word fuck when it's needed.

With AI taking over many of the mundane jobs we humans used to have to do, businesses are becoming increasingly reliant on innovative ideas to survive. And it's people who deliver those ideas. Also, if you are dreaming of a £1m turnover inside three years, then you won't be doing it alone. Hiring the right talent will have to be a huge priority, so ensuring you have access to and can attract good people is key.

When you do start building your team, it adds an extra layer of happiness to your work life. I am honoured and humbled that such talented individuals have joined my business, and watching them grow has been a true joy.

But in Year One, it's most likely just you on your own most days. You have no one to celebrate the wins and commiserate the losses with. To take the edge off the loneliness, I was advised at this stage to get a dog. My wife didn't want a dog, so I borrowed one from a friend. Ralf Dolan was my first team member and we had lots of cuddles in the dark times. He was appointed head of HR and holds that post to this day.

A beautiful, loyal, short, hairy chap with a big tongue, Ralf was happy to follow me around the house. I loved him so much, I let him poo in the garden and happily congratulated him as I picked it up in a sandwich bag. I haven't recruited anyone since who earned that liberty.

Do you understand people?

Reputation is built by the people inside the business, but so few businesses treat their people well. Practically everyone moans about their employer, line manager, work colleagues, hours, workspace or the view out of the window. Most business leaders know that they need to focus on employee wellbeing, but often they follow antiquated systems that are supposed to highlight how to improve it, so they are terrible at delivering a truly positive people strategy. Despite mental health clearly being impacted by this, most employment is still too rigid.

> Key learning: This is your business, so you can choose to have happy employees, and to be happy with the people you work with.

When you start recruiting, you won't really get much choice about who to work with. Choose the best of the bunch and focus on getting them to like you. The best way to get people to like you is to be honest, kind and helpful, and listen to them with the aim of understanding them.

Truly understanding people and what motivates them will be vital in the coming years, so use Year One to meet and interact with many different types of people. Are they driven by money or purpose?

To understand what motivates most people at work, what makes them choose a job and stay in it, remember the acronym CRIMP: credibility, respect, influence, money and power. All these things are important if you want to be happy at work, but the key is the order of priority. If credibility and respect are the most important things to you, then it's likely you and I would get on in a team environment. If your focus is primarily on money and power, then we probably wouldn't.

> Key learning: Look for people who align with your CRIMP priorities. It's likely your values will appeal to them.

Collect personality traits that you adore. This is the start of the process that will help you identify your future teammates. My team members come from all over the place. I started with people who had worked for me in the past, but once that pool was dry, I needed to identify lots of great people long before I could offer them a job. By recognising the qualities you look for in people, you are creating your own dream checklist for the future.

This is my list of criteria for recruiting people. It's not in any particular order as I want *all* these qualities, not just some of them.

- Loyalty
- Honesty
- Humour
- Ambition
- Independence
- Creativity
- Resilience
- Love

The people you need first

Before you can hire anyone, you need clients and customers. Business happens when people get to know, like, trust and respect you, so you need to treat clients and customers with the utmost respect to build a sustainable business. It's quite simple – treat others as you would like to be treated yourself.

Key learning: Be the kindest, nicest person in the room.

At the start, your reputation is down to you, so it should be easy to maintain. You're not an arsehole, so it's vital that you don't act like one if you want anyone to do business with you. When you have a team, it's trickier, but by then, you should have your company values firmly in place.

Good partnerships and business relationships are based on shared morals, values and ethics. Get an understanding of what makes people tick. If you have humour in your armoury, use that to the best of your ability. Making people laugh can gain you huge progress points towards building a relationship.

You can form relationships on social media if real-life networking is problematic. If you're not on LinkedIn, create an account. You need to take it seriously. It's not Instagram or Facebook; it's where you show the people you want to do business with that you know what you stand for and what you care about. Be generous in engaging with other people's posts. As successful businessman and author Daniel Priestley says, persistence beats perfection,[9] so remember this when you start posting. People might not like or comment on your posts at first, but never give up.

---

9   D Priestley, *Key Person of Influence: The five-step method to become one of the most highly valued and highly paid people in your industry* (Rethink Press, 2014)

You will spend most of your time in Year One chasing prospective clients, so do your research before you pitch or meet someone for the first time. I am amazed how many people don't check my LinkedIn profile before they meet me, even when they're interviewing for a role.

> **Key learning: If you are well prepared, you will impress people at a basic level.**

Be warned, though: there will be people you pitch to who just want to steal your ideas or information. They will ask good questions and get you to share everything you've got, keep you on the hook, keep asking for more, making you believe there will be a lovely, shiny new client at the end of the process. This will happen a lot. It's fine. It is all going to build your resilience and your mental strength.

Even when you have been tricked into handing over all of your ideas, you can still take something positive from the situation. You are unique. You and only you can truly deliver your ideas to the market. If someone steals your ideas, they most likely won't get them to work, simply because they are not as committed to them as you are.

You can always have more ideas. When it happens, let it go. Move on and move up.

Who's the boss?

It is a privilege to run your own company, but not having a boss is a massive change if you've been in employment up until now and it will take some adjustment. The best way of progressing in a corporate environment is to do what your boss tells you, do it well and on time. If your boss is a dick, you move departments to work for a less dickish boss and do what they say instead. Either way, in a corporate world, your boss owns you. Curating your own gig without anyone telling you what to do can be disconcerting for even the most driven individuals. You need to know you are the right person to thrive in that environment.

As soon as you get a client, customer or employee, they are essentially your boss. You need to ensure they are more than happy, more than satisfied with you as an individual and your company or brand, because otherwise, they will simply walk away, and that can be devastating. If they're not happy, you're not earning and there's no safety net, no monthly salary to fall back on. It's you and only you who can make it happen.

Hang on, though, *everyone* is your boss? All that work to get away from doing what incompetent people tell you to do, and now you have everybody telling you what to do? Not exactly, because you have the freedom to choose. You are driving the bus, which may have unruly schoolkids and critical passengers on it, but you get to decide who gets on and off. Ultimately, that's anyone who doesn't treat you with the respect you deserve. If you can work out who to kick off the bus quickly, that's a gift.

Choosing who to work with

One of the main privileges of running your own business is the freedom that you now have to only work with people you want to work with. You might have to settle for less than ideal at first, but you and you alone get to choose who you do business with.

> Key learning: You can walk away from toxic partnerships if – and only if – you are not driven by money.

Because my business isn't driven by me wanting to be rich, I can make the difficult decision to leave something if it doesn't feel right. This is such an important mindset to have when starting out.

Doing the right thing – the hard thing – is what will bring you happiness and success. It will also bring you respect. It's the pure definition of freedom. I remind myself of this every day – especially when I'm going through the detoxification process of exiting bad business relationships. If you want to be rich, you will definitely have to work with arseholes from time to time. It's as simple as that.

One of the risks when you choose to work only with non-arseholes is that you may sign a contract with an amazing client company, and then your nice contact leaves and is replaced by an arsehole. This has happened to me more than once. All you can do is focus on the person sitting opposite you and make working with you so rewarding, they don't want to leave.

Assuming your arsehole radar is intact and you walk away from clients who do not respect you, all should go well if you deliver what you said you would. If you are delivering and the client is becoming difficult, it's a communication problem – are they expecting something you're not expecting to deliver? This needs a conversation.

> Key learning: Never shy away from difficult conversations.

If the client is expecting something you can't deliver, be honest and explain why you can't deliver. Is it capacity, time, budget, resource or capability? Maybe you have oversold your services (most starter-uppers do). Your reputation is the most important element you have in your business in the early days, and if you have unhappy clients, your reputation is at risk. If you are out of your depth, you are better off walking away than continuing to damage your reputation. Be honest and live to fight another day.

> Key learning: Never put your reputation at risk – if you make a mistake, own up, be honest and explain why you can't deliver.

One mouth, two ears

Have you ever felt exhausted from talking too much in a meeting? Or looked at the audience of a presentation you are delivering and seen dull faces looking back at you? If you have bored yourself, imagine for a moment how the listener feels.

You may like talking a lot and almost certainly have a lot you want to communicate as a business founder. You're passionate about your idea, but that leads to the risk you'll over-complicate, over-explain, over-sell it, and generally bamboozle your listener.

> Key learning: Bite your tongue. Talk less. We have two ears and one mouth for a reason.

Follow the pattern of 66% listening and 33% talking. Your interactions will be much more impactful and effective. And when you're listening, *really* listen. Don't sit patiently waiting to respond or debunk or challenge what your prospect is saying. Listen to understand why they are saying it.

Nobody likes being sold to, but we mostly like buying things. Understand the prospect's problem through active listening, and then solve it for them. If you nail this, your sales will go through the roof.

And if you do realise you have bored a roomful of people, remember there are no bad days, only days where bad things happen. Try talking less next time.

Are you the right person?

There's not much you can do to fix other people, but you can make sure you are giving yourself the best possible chance of success. The most important qualities you require from Day One to build a £1m business within three years are set out below.

Some can be acquired or developed, but some of them need to be in-built.

I have put them in order of priority this time:

1. Resilience (including tenacity and patience)
2. Drive
3. Self-belief/ positivity
4. The ability to influence and inspire others (leadership)
5. Passion

We have touched on resilience a number of times already, and it's something you absolutely must have when planning and running your startup. Without resilience, you won't survive the many setbacks that will come your way – the arseholes masquerading as clients, the reluctant payers, the many 'no' responses to get that one precious 'yes', to name but a few. You have to pick yourself up after each and every setback, learn from it and keep going. No one ever said this running your own business thing was easy, but if you have or develop the resilience to make it work, it will be so worth it.

Drive and self-belief pretty much speak for themselves. No one ever made a success in business without the drive to make it work and the belief that they and only they could do it. Be positive. You can do this. Believe in your ability, your drive, your idea. The business world is waiting for you.

Leadership qualities come into their own more as your business grows and you put together your team. Your boss list will help you here: add the qualities you admired in your former bosses to your armoury, and make sure you never adopt the qualities you despised. In short, don't be an arsehole.

Passion is a funny thing – everyone is passionate about something, even if they have a reputation for being laid back. Passion for your business and your mission is vital when you fly your own plane, but it can't be faked.

If you're not passionate, that is going to be an issue for you if you want to build, lead and inspire a team. If you're not passionate about the change you are going to make – that is catastrophic.

If business is all about the people, you need to ask yourself: are you the right person to start your own business? Do you have the right qualities? What are your chances of developing them quickly? What has your environment given you, both the one around you today and the one you were born into?

You can adapt to any environment, but how you were brought up is a huge factor. Being a parent myself has highlighted the importance of my own parents in defining who I am as a person: my morals, my ethics, my beliefs.

Having a professional working mother was a key element in the lucky soup I was served on my journey. My mother is an incredible woman: hardcore, direct, powerful and independent. Never one to shy away from issues, but also supportive, caring and loving: a great balance of skills to have.

She worked full time as a microbiologist. I learned my work ethic from my summer jobs in her lab, but the biggest learning was from rare visits to the main lab where she was developing and testing medicines. I found it fascinating seeing her in this envi-ronment. This was my mum – the woman who I had treated like a slave for most of my life – as a powerful, influential professional who other people looked up to.

My father became managing director of the family business, Joseph Miller and Sons, at the age of thirty-three, inheriting an overwhelming task of turning around a complex fourth-generation business. Most family businesses die in the third generation because the blood bonds of cousins don't tend to be as strong as those of siblings. Dad inherited a million problems and dealt with them during incredibly stressful times: a recession, the three-day week and power shortages of the 1970s.

He applied adaptability and flexibility – the skills that will allow you to win with your startup – to an eighty-year-old business. In fifty-five years' service – his whole career – he managed unbe-lievable restructuring projects, moving the business four times and reshaping the revenue model regularly. He dragged the company from 1963 through to 2018, and leaves a legacy of a business 130 years in existence.

My dad is the most resilient human I know. As a child, I got to follow his journey through surviving and building a business back up, and it's only now that I can appreciate the advantage that has given me.

Key learning: Take all the learnings and advantages you can from your upbringing to give yourself a head start in business.

I appreciate the odds were stacked in my favour. There are so many people who invested their time and effort into making me who I am today. My success in business is a small part of proving to all these people that their investment was worth it.

And yet, even with all the stars aligned, starting and running my business has pushed me way beyond my limits. I've found it tougher than I could have imagined, and I can imagine a lot.

If you didn't start off in life with these advantages, be aware that some of your competitors will have done, and you are going to have to find ways to acquire for yourself what others have been given for free. Just know that your success when you achieve it will be all the more rewarding.

Whoever you are, whatever your background, you'll have to have a support system. Your support system will need to include your partner, if you have one; we'll discuss in the next chapter how to make sure you still have a partner at the end of Year One. But when it's time to jump, to commit to your new life, only you can make that leap.

Can you jump?

Regardless of your heritage, your upbringing, your environment, the bundles of cash in your survival fund, the purpose, values and USP you have crafted and your incredible resilience, you still have to jump off the cliff and actually do this. The moment when you look over the edge is one that will stay with you for a long time.

I distinctly remember my moment at sunset on 11 March 2014. This was the moment I finally knew in my head I was actually going to do it. I was going to launch my startup. After two years flailing in Year Zero, I was going to jump.

I had been planning my startup for more than ten years in total, seriously for two years and uber-seriously for more than a year. I had talked and talked, creating lovely brand logos and layouts, and refining models and approaches, but there were always a few more things to do before I handed my notice in at work. But deep down, I was merely terrified of actually jumping off the cliff.

Key learning: Planning can easily turn into procrastinating.

What took me so long? I spent ages trying to convince others to join me on the journey and take some of the risk on their shoulders. I preferred the model of three founders, which makes decision making easier, but finding even one other person to come on the startup journey and share the responsibility is hard. Finding two co-founders is probably ten times harder.

I went through several threesomes and rejected them all, which probably cost me (or maybe bought me) six extra months of planning. Why did I waste six months trying to convince others to come into business with me? If I'm honest, I was looking for a safety net, another hurdle to jump through before I had to face the crippling fear of hurling myself into the unknown.

However long you plan and talk about starting your own business, however long you put off actually resigning from the safety of a salary every month, one day, you are going to have to take the leap of faith. Every single person who has succeeded in their own business went through the same fear.

> Key learning: At some point, you will have to act.

It's likely you will only have one shot at starting a business. It's so hard to start something once, let alone more than once. Some say you gain so much from starting a business and failing that when you go for it a second time, you are better at it. That may be true if you're young and have plenty of time to sink back into the world of working for someone else before giving it a second try, but most successful people start their business later in life, which doesn't give them the luxury of time.

It's lonely on the cliff edge, but with resilience, drive, self-belief and passion, the initial drop won't feel impossible to survive. You just need to give yourself the final push that tips the balance. It's like doing a bungee jump. You can see the ground below you and you actually have to be the one to make the decision to jump.

You lean in, your knees bend, your toes leave the edge and you are away. Your stomach goes first, then the rest of you follows. Gulp!

CHEAT SHEET

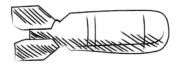

Congratulations, you've taken the leap. Or at least, you're ready to, so let's have a look at what we have covered in this chapter to encourage you to step over the edge.

- You're entering the privileged world of no commuting, no racing with the rats and no having to jump when your boss says jump. You are free – truly free for the first time in your professional life.

- Ask yourself today if you think you are the right person to build your startup, considering your background, upbringing and environment. You will need every advantage you can get.

- Get a Ralf. He changed my life in the lonely early months. He's loyal, honest, funny, ambitious, independent (sort of), creative, resilient and loving. The perfect number two.

- If you want to remember what motivates people in business, think CRIMP. If you're driven by earning credibility and respect above all other types of remuneration, then you've got this. You will have purpose and your chances of success have just trebled.

❖ When you're building your team, your values will be worth their weight in gold in their ability to attract the right people.

❖ Take the brave decision to leave the arseholes behind and extract yourself from toxic business relationships. Work with the people you want to work with.

❖ Keep your clients happy and get the all-important word-of-mouth recommendations by making sure you deliver on what you promise.

❖ If, for some reason, your clients are not happy when you are delivering all you have promised, make sure you have an honest conversation with them. Are they expecting more? If you cannot meet their expectations, tell them.

❖ Do you have the balls to actually jump off that cliff edge? It seems so easy when you're not standing on it, but it's time to face it for real. It's one of life's true before and after moments.

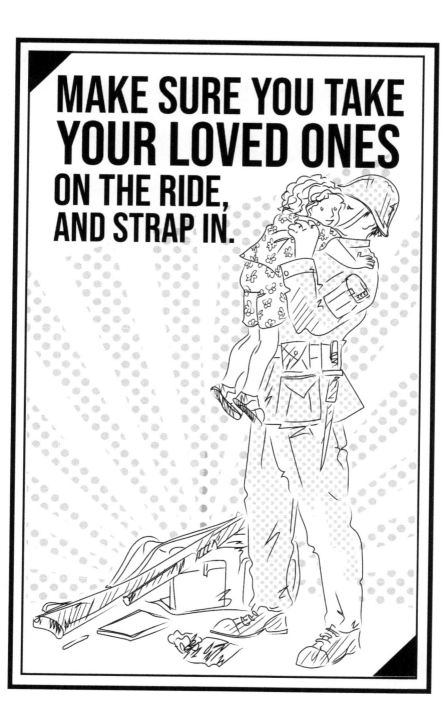

7

YOUR STARTUP AND YOUR PRIVATE LIFE

This chapter is for both starter-uppers and their long-suffering significant others and family members. If you have a life partner, and more importantly would like to continue to have one, get them to read it, especially if you're living together, even more so if you have kids. Or get your parent(s) to read it if you've moved back in with them to save money, or if it looks like you will never be able to leave home.

Perhaps you're living with housemates whom you like and don't want to piss off. Perhaps your housemates are also starter-uppers, in which case, good luck. You all need to be kind to one another. Whatever your living circumstances, this chapter is intended to help those around you understand more about the change that has happened to you, and will subsequently happen to them.

I will focus on the relationship with a significant other as that's where I have the most experience. Whether or not you have children or live together, you and your partner both need to understand that your new business will affect your relationship. There's no avoiding it. The mental capacity required to start and grow a business will take chunks out of your brain that you could previously focus on treating your partner like a king or queen.

Managing your family life and work life

You may already have been doing a stressful job that made you an unsatisfactory partner, in which case both you and your significant other will understand the impact work can have on your personal life somewhat. But when you start a new business, this impact rises to a whole new level, because you are entirely responsible for its success and it's likely you'll do much of the work in your home.

Once you add children into the mix, the effects of the business-related upheaval are even more significant. Is starting both a business and a family at the same time a good idea or not? Timing is key, as always, but it can often be having children that eventually convinces a dreamer to take the leap off the cliff and start up. I bow to those legends who start up while caring for young children – we mere mortals are not worthy.

In my case, my wife and I felt it was vital to get the business underway before we had children. I had eighteen months of caring for my business baby before I finally met my real babies, which strangely was the same amount of time I had given myself before my survival money ran out.

Children provide context and reality to the wider stresses of running a business. I have twins, which means it's intense and all-consuming when I am in Daddy mode. Then, I honestly don't have time to think or worry about the business.

When I'm in business-founder mode, it's also all-consuming, so then I don't have time to think or worry about the twins. It's like there are two versions of me in one body and I need to make sure I jump back and forth without falling or tripping. But I have always been disciplined with the two parts of my life, and to me, that is key to managing mental health.

Key learning: Recognise the importance of both work life and family life. Whichever one you are concentrating on, give it your all.

For example, I have just left this writing lark for half an hour to go and play with my kids. That's thirty minutes enjoying real life and real pleasures, blowing up balloons and letting them fly off around the room. Over and over again. I actually feel quite lightheaded. But it's a privilege that I have earned by having control of my time.

Children or no children, starting a business is doable. There's no magic formula, but having a solid relationship with a partner does mean you are likely to be more grounded, more level-headed and more able to succeed. The love of your partner will absolutely help you through the dark times.

Get your partner to read this next section. It's based on what I would say to my own wife to enable her to understand why I do what I do, maybe to make me feel better about what I have put her through. Either way, unless you truly are a lone wolf, it's probably the most important part of this book.

Loved ones, this section is for you

Your partner's starting a business? Well, that's just great! They were doing a good job, earning money, getting out of the house and making a dent in the universe. The bills were paid, money was coming in, everything was hunky-dory. And now they've gone and fucked it all up.

The good news for you is that all of the stress, tears, missed events and bullshit of their first year in business has *nothing* to do with you. Unless you are one of the rare breed of partners who encouraged the startup. If that's you, then you have no excuses. Most of you won't have chosen this new life that is being thrust upon you, and the chances are you will never go back to the life you once enjoyed.

If your partner succeeds, then they won't be the same person they once were; they will be a far greater version of themselves, able to achieve everything they'd ever dreamed of. Sounds good, right?

But bear in mind that the majority of new businesses fail. While this is the less favourable option, it is something to prepare yourself for. If this happens, your partner may go back into the wider world of work, perhaps doing what they did before, perhaps finding another new career. They will have missed out on progression in the corporate machine (or whatever their career path was) and will see their former peers ahead of them, further up the ladder. Even worse, the buzz that they felt from running their own gig will have gone, leaving a sense of failure and a need to understand why they failed. That is, until they start their second business.

I'm sure you don't want to have to see them go through that, so your support and love for them during this journey is key to pushing them into the former category of starter-uppers: those who succeed. The partners of starter-uppers are heroes. There are many successful entrepreneurs who cite their partner as their rock, the real reason they succeeded.

> Key learning: As the long-suffering partner of a starter-upper, your love and support is vital to their success.

There's no warning, no manual, nothing that can prepare you for what you are about to face. It's so tough loving a dreamer, but if that dreamer believes they are actually going to achieve their dreams, it's even tougher. Get ready. You may not have bought a ticket for the ride, but you are in the front row of the roller-coaster and it's going to be an excitingly terrifying trip.

The partner's guide to Year Zero

You may have been hearing about your partner's startup dream for a while. My wife had been hearing about my dream from the day we first met. I hope you have been discussing it in depth, as this is a huge decision for both of you.

Before they embark on Year Zero, the run-up to jumping off the cliff, there are some things you need to discuss with your partner. How do you each define success? What is it that you both want to achieve that determines success or failure? It's good to be aligned in your definition and to have common goals, so agree what would warrant success. Make it achievable, at least to start with, and the goals will give you some milestones to hold your partner accountable.

Key learning: Agree with your partner what success means to both of you.

Here are some more things you need to talk about (but make your partner do most of the talking). Why are they doing this? What is driving them to quit their secure full-time job and start up a startup? What is the vision they want to achieve? What values do they want their startup to stand for? Is this purely about money? Changing your lives? A better life-work balance?

How long has your partner been in the planning stage? Is this a whim or something that they feel they were born to do? Is this an itch that could go away? Should you encourage it to go away? Have you actually been holding them back by explaining your reasons why they shouldn't do it?

Your role as partner of a starter-upper in Year Zero is vital. Be devil's advocate. Challenge them constantly about why and how they believe their startup will work when so many don't. They may not like it, but they are likely to thank you for it one day.

Before I started my company, I used to advise everyone to start a company. Now if someone says they are planning a startup, I just ask them why they're doing it. If your partner honestly feels they were born to do this thing and has unbelievable resilience and drive, don't even try to stop them. Resilience is the first thing they will need to actually make their crazy dream real.

When you have got to the point of exhaustion from explaining rationally why you think your partner's business idea won't work, bored to death of hearing them talk about it (get used to that), bored of hearing them moaning about their current situation, their work, their commute, their boss, you have done your duty. Now it's time to flip to 100% support. They are going on an emotional rollercoaster and you need to be the shoulder they can lean on.

Zero negativity is key when they do finally jump off the cliff, quit their job and start up their business. Believe that your partner is going to be one of the successful ones. They will go on to achieve greatness, and they won't be able to do it without you. You will be their number-one supporter and that merits a huge amount of credit. Remember the importance of *your* role in *their* success.

> Key learning: If they're really going to do this startup thing, your wholehearted support will be an essential part of your partner's success.

Once Year Zero is over and your partner arrives at Year One, the fun really starts.

Working from home

The words 'I'm working from home tomorrow' always used to unleash the green-eyed monster in the office environment. Now that many more people work from home, this doesn't happen so much. You might be working from home for an employer while your partner is starting up. Perhaps you both used to be out of the house all day, and you still are while your partner is starting their plan for world domination from the spare room or the kitchen table. Perhaps your work culture doesn't favour working from home and your bosses distrust employees who do.

If you're both working from home, who is considered to be 'busy with work'? The starter-upper or the wage slave? If something domestic needs to happen in working hours, like having the boiler serviced, who deals with it? If the doorbell rings unexpectedly, who answers it? How do you make sure you both have the space and the broadband you need to work?

> Key learning: Agree responsibilities if you both work from home so neither one of you is left doing the lion's share of the household tasks on top of your work commitments.

Starting a business from home is not the same as working from home. Your live-in starter-upper is not a cleaner, a cook, a parcel receiver, a handyperson, a washing specialist, a tidy-upper, a lounger, a loafer or a fraud. Your beloved is certainly not waiting for a list of tasks from you.

Yes, if they are slick and efficient and nice, they can take on a bigger share of the household tasks – after all, they're not commuting any more, or reporting to a boss any more, so their stress has reduced immeasurably overnight. But don't assume that they're not working as hard as you just because no one is making them keep to a schedule.

Try not to begrudge or be jealous of your starter-upper. It may appear you are now living with a bum, but one day that bum could achieve their dreams. They could be truly happy. And you love them, right? So you want them to be happy and achieve their dreams. That is the whole point of being in a loving relationship.

You will be instrumental in their success. If they love you now, they will love you a whole lot more if you are still together in five years' time.

How to stay in a relationship when you run a business from home

It was September 2014 when I quit my job. Winter was coming and I would be working from home forevermore, so the hell of the morning routine was just a nasty memory for me. Why shouldn't I start my day watching a bit of TV in bed? It only took me a minute to get to my laptop.

When I first started my business, I used to stay in bed while my poor wife got up when her alarm shrieked, walked bleary-eyed into the shower, made herself even more beautiful to the world and dragged herself out the door into the commuting hell. I can remember once asking if she would mind not turning all the lights on while she was getting ready. I didn't ask again.

If you want to stay in your loving relationship when you start a business, get out of bed before your partner. Get up, make them a cup of tea or coffee, scrape the ice off the car – do everything possible that could make their morning easier. Ignore this advice if you like arguments and want to split up. There is nothing more frustrating for anyone than going through their morning routine while their partner stays comfy and warm in bed, updating them on Piers Morgan's latest rant.

Getting out of bed first is a small show of commitment to your partner while they're working hard and bringing home the bacon so that you can follow your dreams. It's the least you can do. If they work away from home, get up and show commitment before they leave, and then go back to bed. Remember you can do that – it's not going to make you successful, but you can do it. If you do it once they've gone, a) they won't know and b) you'll not piss them off from the first moment of the day.

I'm sorry to say that pretty much everything else you do during the early days is likely to piss them off. There is no substitute for the commute. However hard you have worked, in the back of their mind, they are still likely to be jealous that you've sat around in a tracksuit all day while they've been out working. They will imagine you climbing back into bed while they're crammed on the Tube or stuck in traffic.

> Key learning: Do everything you can in your day to make your partner's life easier.

Happiness

The overall goal is for you and your partner to be even more happy together because of your business, not less happy. For that, you need to agree on the most difficult of questions: what is the meaning of life? Yes, that old chestnut. If you can't agree on it, you have to at least see one another's point of view.

The meaning of happiness in professional life has two parts:

1. Identifying what makes you happy and pursuing that relentlessly
2. Helping those less fortunate than yourself

Simple.

So many of us follow the system – school, good grades, university, job, work hard, career, family, retire, death. Wow, what a journey. We've followed the system and won. We can pat ourselves on the back and post about it all over social media, but this is not reality.

It's always interesting to ask someone if they like their job. Many reply, 'Yeah, I love my job', but those same people also moan about it all the time. I know I did. I spent fifteen years loving my job and moaning about it. My friends called me Moaning Mewart. I was a lot of fun in those days.

Starting your own business should make you happy, even in the dark times. Experiences make you happier than things. When you buy something – a watch, jacket, car, whatever – you love your shiny new toy for a while. You've earned it and you enjoy it. The trouble is, over time, that happiness wanes. You get used to the thing you once loved so much. It gets a scratch. It needs cleaning or repairing. It turns into just another thing you own and need to look after, find space for or get rid of.

When you experience something – a gig, a festival or a night out, for example – it also brings you joy, particularly if you do it with other people. You remember the fun and happiness every now and then, and say to yourself, 'Yeah, that was a great experience and it made me happy.'

Over time, the memory grows and you become fonder and fonder of that particular experience. The brain tends to delete or fade out the negative parts of the experience (waiting for a taxi, getting soaked, eating a cold kebab) while promoting the laughs and positive moments, and happiness grows from that memory.

Key learning: Experiences are far more enjoyable than material possessions.

And you, my friend, are close to embarking on one of the greatest experiences of your life. Make sure you are taking your loved ones on the ride with you and strap in. You have two chapters to go, and then it's over to you.

CHEAT SHEET

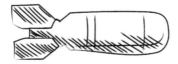

This chapter has spoken as much to your partner as to you. Here's a quick recap for you both:

⚙ As a starter-upper, learn to balance your work life and your home life. When you spend time with your partner and/or children, make sure you're fully present. The same goes for the time you dedicate to your business.

⚙ The partner of a starter-upper has the power to tip the balance in favour of their dreams coming true.

⚙ When you start your business, you're likely to be working from home. If your partner is still working full time or caring for the kids, do everything you can to make their life better. Share out the chores and treat them with the respect they deserve. Delight, surprise and impress them as much as you can.

⚙ As the partner – act as devil's advocate for as long as possible, reminding your loved one of all the risks involved in starting up a business, but if the idea just won't go away, get behind it fully.

✧   As the starter-upper – convince your partner this is the right thing to do. They will be your fiercest critic, so this is your first step on the pitching ladder.

✧   As the partner – do not give your live-in starter-upper task lists every day. Even though they may be at home all day in a tracksuit, they're still working.

✧   Both of you, remember that happiness is about experiences, not things.

MONEY WON'T MAKE YOU HAPPY.

FREEDOM AND TIME WILL.

8

MENTAL HEALTH AND MENTAL STRENGTH

Founding a company is bad for your health, both mental and physical. Not the most comforting start to a chapter, I admit, but it's not all bad news. I am going to explain how you can manage this and even turn it to your advantage.

Information and knowledge are your most powerful allies in the assault on your brain and physique that every starter-upper goes through. Experience allows you to build your own generator for when you need to power up.

Owning and managing your physical health while you're scheming away on your masterplan is something that is within your control. Go for a run or get some weights – simple, if you commit to it. Owning and managing your mental health is less easy.

I have lived through mental challenges I thought I could not handle, but I did. Your resilience is your most powerful asset when you're managing your mind – the old mantra of never, ever giving up is the rope to cling to in the dark times. In this chapter, I will outline some of the other tools that have helped me to manage my mental health, all of which are easy to put into practice.

Mental health and our understanding of it is a major challenge of our time. We are winning the first skirmishes in that war – many of us are more comfortable talking about mental health openly – but we still have a long way to go.

National mental-health statistics are alarming in general. Mind, the biggest mental-health charity, says that more than one in three of us will suffer from some form of mental illness in our lifetime.[10] Mental illness is still such a taboo subject that those statistics will probably only grow over time as we understand our brains more.

The numbers become downright terrifying for starter-uppers. According to a study by Michael Freeman, founders of companies are 50% more likely to report having a mental-health condition, with some specific conditions being incredibly prevalent.[11] They are:

---

10   J Chapman, 'Investors and entrepreneurs need to address the mental health crisis in startups' (Extra Crunch, 2018)
11   M Freeman, 'Are entrepreneurs "touched with fire"?', www.michaelafreemanmd.com, 2015, www.michaelafreemanmd.com/Research_files/Are%20Entrepreneurs%20Touched%20with%20Fire%20(pre-pub%20n)%204-17-15.pdf

- ✧ Twice as likely to suffer from depression
- ✧ Twice as likely to have psychiatric hospitalisation
- ✧ Twice as likely to have suicidal thoughts
- ✧ Six times more likely to suffer from attention deficit hyperactivity disorder (ADHD)
- ✧ Three times more likely to suffer from substance abuse
- ✧ Ten times more likely to suffer from bi-polar disorder

That sounds scary, right? But remember, knowledge is power.

> Key learning: Being aware of both the state of your mental health and the limits of your mental strength gives you the power to avoid worsening the statistics.

Rope and elastic

In her TEDxOcala talk 'The Secret of Becoming Mentally Strong',[12] psychotherapist and clinical social worker Amy Morin explains that the difference between mental strength and mental health becomes easier to understand when you compare it to physical strength and physical health. Building bigger muscles can improve your physical strength, but big muscles don't help you deal with a specific physical health problem like high cholesterol. For that, you need specific treatment.

Morin brilliantly explains how you can improve your mental

---

12   A Morin, 'The secret of becoming mentally strong', TEDx, 2020, www.youtube.com/watch?v=TFbv757kup4

health by reviewing both your positive and negative mental habits. But, she points out, you gain wisdom and insights from the experience of mental strain, which can also be valuable.

Consider your mental strength – the ability to cope with upsetting or frustrating events and negative emotions in a healthy way – like a piece of rope, and the things you need to do are weights hanging on the rope. If you keep hanging more and more weights on the rope, it becomes taut. Your mental strength can be trained and improved by the weights you add as you gain experience.

When you understand yourself better, you will recognise when you have overloaded your rope. When your rope is strained, you can learn how to lighten the load, use your additional wisdom to pause to weave a thicker rope, and then go again.

At any age, your mental strength has a preferred effective weight load. During the early years of your startup, when you have the time and energy, work out what your limit is, and then work on using experience to increase that limit. Consider it as being like building bigger brain muscles.

If you persistently overload your rope without giving yourself enough lightening intervals, you will strain your mental capacity. Often mental strain will manifest in physical strain. Your body will warn you through poor sleep, worry, bad diet, addictions, aches, pains and so on.

Key learning: Recognising how your body is talking to you is vital to identifying the limits of your mental strength.

Consider your mental health more like a piece of elastic than a rope. Your brain's mental capacity is malleable, affected by the excitement of new ventures. An overwhelming passion for a cause or purpose allows it to stretch, and then bounce back up when the pressure is alleviated.

When you are truly on your own and not wrapped in the comfort blanket of the payroll, you get to see how far your mental-health elastic can stretch. Be prepared for it to stretch more than you thought it would, maybe even more than you thought possible. This might be a new feeling for you, but it does not have to be scary, as long as you know the limits of your personal elastic. If you over-stretch, your elastic won't spring back to its original form.

There is a benefit to overstretching your mental capacity: it can change you forever, in a good way. I have done it more than once, but do it too much and, like your mental-strength rope, your elastic will snap.

When you're hanging matching weights on your mental-strength rope and mental-health elastic, make sure you recognise and align the impact of both. Doing so will allow you to navigate this tricky path. Fortunately, you can gather some handy weapons into your armoury which will improve your mental strength and mental health at the same time. Here are some of my favourites.

Positivity

I used to be a pessimist before I read *The Secret* by Rhonda Byrne.[13] Its premise is simple: in short, positivity is infectious. The more positive you are, the more likely it is that positive things will happen to you.

I started work on changing my mindset about eighteen months before I started my business. Ant Middleton, the ex-soldier presenter of Channel 4's *Who Dares Wins*, speaks of zero negativity as a mantra for everything he has achieved,[14] and he is not one to disagree with.

> Key learning: Zero negativity, or 100% positive mindset, makes a real difference in the startup world.

Meditation

I recommend a daily meditation practice for anyone considering starting a company. Every person's journey is different, but meditation will help you more than you can possibly understand until you've tried it. Sign up for a startup course to give you deeper understanding. Then I recommend you find an app that works for you.

---

13   R Byrne, *The Secret* (Simon & Schuster, 2006)
14   A Middleton, *Zero Negativity: The power of positive thinking* (HarperCollins Publishers, 2020)

I find meditation hard. It took me five years of practice to finally get better at it, but I kept going because from the start, I reaped rewards in every aspect of my life, particularly business.

Key learning: Meditation can help anyone and everyone in the startup world. Even if you find it difficult at first, stick with it.

Exercise

I fail at this almost every day. It helps if you can build walking into your daily routine so that it doesn't just appear on your to-do list. Walk the dog, walk the kids to school, or just take a walk by yourself.

Key learning: Do something that gets you into the fresh air, ideally in the morning to clear the mind.

Music

I have been addicted to music since childhood, particularly when I can listen without distractions on headphones. Lyrics are really important to me.

For as long as I can remember, I have used music to help me understand my emotions, and since I started my company, it's been a huge emotional support in good and bad times. I have created playlists for each year of the business. There is a song for every mood and I have a specific playlist for big meetings.

> Key learning: Create playlists of music that's guaranteed to lift you up when times get tough.

Love and faith

I am lucky to be surrounded by love – I hope you are, too. The love you receive, and the love you have for others, will be a godsend when you most need it. Love and kindness are central to the practices of all the main world religions for a reason.

I'm not a religious person, so all the faith I need comes from those I love and those who love me. Love and faith will remind you why you started this crazy thing in the first place. Heavy is the head that wears the crown, but love makes it more comfortable, so treat everyone you meet with respect and love. This will make both you and them happier. A little hug for the mind.

> Key learning: Do whatever you need to do to give you faith, as by Jove, you are going to need it.

Laughter

If laughter is the medicine, humour is the ambulance. If you can laugh at yourself, laugh with others and laugh in the face of disaster, you will build your resilience fast.

> Key learning: Laugh at yourself. It will make the hard times less unbearable and make your personality appealing to those you meet.

Swearing

Fuck, in my humble opinion, is the best word in the English language. It has more uses than any other, from offending people to emphasising just how good life can be. According to a study by Dr David Stillwell, a lecturer in Big Data Analytics at the University of Cambridge, people who frequently swear are being more honest.[15]

A good old swear-fest will make you feel better, but make sure you mirror your client or prospective client when you're in their company. If they swear, go ahead. If they do not, best to avoid it. And never use the C word. Save that for those who truly deserve it.

> Key learning: In the right context, a fucking good swear-fest is balm for the soul.

Use your addictions positively

Most of us are addicted to something or other. For a lot of people, it's food, alcohol and/or caffeine, but nicotine is making a comeback now that vaping has become widespread. Work

---

15   D Stillwell, 'Study finds link between swearing and honesty', Phys.Org, 2017, https://phys.org/news/2017-01-links-honesty.html

out what your addiction is and how to manage it rather than using it as a lifeline during this stressful time.

I managed to turn the temptation to eat my way out of stress on its head by embracing the feeling of hunger and attaching it to a feeling of desire. I always go into every pitch meeting hungry. The idea that hunger pains are my body eating its own belly fat was hugely influential in me losing two stone in Year Zero. Of course, this is only a good strategy if you have two stone to lose.

Key learning: Recognise your addiction and turn it into a strength.

Never, ever give up

For those who have experienced it, failing and losing the business they have dreamed about for so long can seem to be the worst thing ever to happen to them. But time is a great healer; although the scars will always remain, they will fade.

The only proven way of avoiding failure is never, ever to give up. You will want to. But if you don't, if you dig deep into your resilience bucket, you can adapt and modify your nightmare, turning any situation around.

Key learning: Accept failure in all its forms for what it is – a lesson. Use the lesson to drive you onwards.

Me and my mental health

I'm lucky in that I've avoided the big boys: depression and anxiety. But I am susceptible to stress.

Stress is not officially a mental illness, but it should be in my opinion, as at its worst, constant stress evokes feelings of helplessness and lack of control. I know I am stressed when my brain buzzes and I become more clumsy than usual – I trip over everything, bump into everything and emotionally withdraw from people.

I manage my stress in a selection of ways. They may sound weird, but they work for me, and I suspect many of them will work for you, too. Experiment to find your own stressbusters. You don't need to justify your stress management choices to anyone.

During my most stressed periods, I tend to chant the mantra, 'Too blessed to be stressed'. I came across the use of mantras when I started meditating, and while it's not one of the traditional ones, this one works for me. How dare I be stressed when the world has dumped so much opportunity in my lap?

I also talk to myself. Saying things out loud helps me visualise them more. I look in the mirror for five minutes before I begin my self-talk. It is not easy, but if I do this at the start of the day, i t helps me understand the person I am becoming, the changes I am going to make, my true purpose.

Mundane tasks such as folding the washing or doing the dishes slow down my buzzing brain and keep me grounded. I also have rituals – I used to have a pair of lucky pants, but now I have seven pairs of lucky pants because I like to feel lucky every day. It gives me the opportunity to do lots more washing, too.

I accept that I can only do one thing at a time. Yes, that's possibly because I'm a man; it amazes me that my wife can have three things going on concurrently. If you can multitask, it will be an asset as you grow a business, but you need to know whether you can or can't. If you can't, doing more than one thing at a time will make you more stressed and you will get nothing done.

> Key learning: Experience will show you what stresses you and what alleviates that stress.

My happy place

For me, silence is golden. My favourite and most creative place to work is in my home office/converted garage. A mere 7 metres from my house, it is a quiet sanctuary, my safe place. I am there now, writing, and I feel different.

When my company acquired office space, that also became a creative place for me. In the early days of the first Covid lock-down in 2020, The Point.1888 hadn't yet moved in, but I found my empty office with its four bare white walls a calming place to work, while most of the country's desk workers grappled with doing their day jobs from home.

Along with a calm, silent and clutter-free work environment, transitions and boundaries are important to me in structuring my day. Boundaries are the rules that help you to control your working life, for example – turning all your notifications off on your apps so that you don't get distracted by work stuff when you're in nonwork mode, or setting rules that you won't work past 5.30pm or arrive at work before 9am. They are not easy, but they will manage your long-term sustainability to run the company.

Transitions are normally the first and last 30 minutes of your working day. Avoid meetings and give yourself time to move from one version of yourself to the other. Use this time to check to-do lists, your diary and your plans for the day. Always find some time to reflect at the end of the day – check your key highlights, practise gratitude and congratulate yourself on what you have achieved rather than what is still to be done.

Being faithful to your boundaries and transitions is essential to manage stress.

My notebook habit

As well as being an important resource for my business, my daily note-making is a mental-health management tool inasmuch as it keeps me centred and declutters my mind. Writing notes is hugely important for tracking progress, which is difficult in the early months when you feel that you're floundering, and for mapping out elements of what you consider significant.

I write the significant things that happen each week, both good and bad, into a diary (you can always make voice notes and have them transcribed, if you really hate writing). And I do this religiously. After a month, when I review my notes for a four-week period, I see what I have achieved, and what I thought was important and now realise was irrelevant. Within three months of starting this habit, I had a fascinating insight into a starter-upper's mind, and the notes have become more useful over time. The more thorough the notes, the more invaluable they will be in the future.

When I review a year's worth of notes, I pick out the most significant thing that happened each week. I then name every week after that defining factor, from 'Ill week' to 'Dream client week' to 'Barbados week'. Even after all these years, I can remember why each week was significant and what I learned from it. It helps me keep track of the big picture.

Too many, too much, too far

Why are so many of us mentally troubled? Certainly, more of us now feel able to talk about our mental-health issues openly, which is good, enabling us to list the triggers that can send us into despair. My personal culprits include social media and the grass-is-always-greener feeling it promotes, entitlement, the outdated education system, people who can't accept their own mental-health challenges, the system, the government. I obviously can't do much about any of these triggers, and nor can you do anything to change your own triggers, so we all need to keep our focus solely on what we and we alone can control.

One thing we can control is the number of people we take responsibility for. The number of other humans we are connected with in life today can feel overwhelming. There are too many people from our past (people we've met, cared for or hated, moved on from) all being tipped back into our lives through the power of social media. There are too many people who seem to need us and want a piece of us. Nobody truly disappears from our lives anymore.

The people who really need you are your loved ones (partners, family members and close friends) and employees. You must be a rock to these people, and that's hard enough. If I'm going to be there for my team and be the best leader I can be, for example, plus be there for my wife and children, I might not be a good son, brother or friend sometimes.

> **Key learning:** While being a rock to those who really matter, don't try to be a rock to everyone you know on LinkedIn or Facebook, too. You can't do it all.

Choose those from across your entire digital network who are making your life happy, and bin the rest. This can feel harsh when you apply it to long-standing acquaintances, but as you progress on your founder journey, it will become clear that you have changed, while people you have known for a long time, even been close to, have not.

> **Key learning:** While you're becoming the person you want to be, many people you have known for years are not.

We often believe that our oldest friends are our most important ones; in fact, it's rare that this is the case. Friendships are conditional. Some will come and go; some will get stronger; new people will appear in your life who you'll wish you had met a long time ago. It is what it is.

> Key learning: Your real friends are the ones who will back you 100% and believe in your dream.

Get your workspace right

This might be your first chance to choose how you want your working environment to be. Get it right for yourself. Find your safe, happy place, your creative place, and spend as much time there as you can.

Some people listen to music at work, some like to chat, others like silence. The set-up you create for work, even at home, needs to replicate the good things about a workplace – you have space that is only for work and is conducive to how you work best. Find a corner, spare room or shed for your workspace, preferably somewhere you can't see from the 'home life' part of your day. If your desk is at the end of your bed, get a screen or turn your bed around so that you aren't staring at your workspace when you wake up.

You also still need a morning routine and transition between home life and work life. That could be a walk around the park or to the corner shop, or twenty minutes listening to music or a podcast, or your meditation time. Replicate the feeling of leaving one part of your life and starting another. Of course, as we discussed in Chapter 7, if you have a partner or share your home with others, you'll need to work out some of the details with them.

It is human nature to question how happy we are in life. Freedom makes me happy. Working for myself and having complete control over my time makes me happy. If the meaning of life is to pursue happiness, then understanding what really makes you happy needs to be on your to-do list for Day One of Year One.

CHEAT SHEET

A tough chapter, but an essential one. Mental health is finally getting the spotlight it deserves, so make sure you look after yours.

- ✛ Learn the limits of your mental health and watch yourself like a hawk.

- ✛ Learn to train your mental strength and resilience over the long term.

- ✛ Everyone has a mental-health issue. Work out what yours is and talk to others about it. Help to destroy the taboo.

- ✛ Recognise what triggers stress in you and discover ways to alleviate that stress.

- ✛ Make notes of what you have done every day as a reminder over time of what you have learned.

- ✛ Find your ideal workspace and set it up to suit you.

- ✛ Realise that old friends are not always best friends. If people are standing still in life while you're moving forward, they may well no longer have a place in your world.

NEVER EVER EVER GIVE UP

THE FIRST RULE OF SURVIVAL

9

YEAR ONE

The time for preparation is done and Year Zero is at an end. You've taken that jump off the cliff, it's Year One and now you have a simple task. *Just Survive Somehow.*

Easy, right?

Tell the world

As you progress in your business, sharing your insights and putting yourself out there will help you build your brand and network. It will also help you make clear choices about how you operate because you have to explain your process to others.

You can do this from the start with LinkedIn articles, or you might think in terms of TED talks, webinars, podcasts, YouTube broadcasts, TikTok videos, Clubhouse drop-ins and other outlets that have not yet been invented. For all these, you need details of your daily life in business, much of which you will (blissfully) forget if you don't record it somewhere.

I would thoroughly recommend you write down the stuff that happens to you on your own journey. Week by week, you will gather material to promote your brand. Everyone has an opinion that is worthy – you are unique. I would encourage you to develop a writing habit, even if you do not intend to publish the results.

I find writing hugely cathartic. The amount of clutter that is now down on paper and no longer in my brain provides me with overwhelming relief. I like to write in silence, normally early in the morning when my mind is at rest. It's so peaceful, which is not something you get to experience often when you are running a company and have a young family.

Above all, the writing process has forced me to face and overcome the self-generated obstacles that beset us all the minute we try to put ourselves out there. This has been my proudest achievement. I found out early in my startup journey that the obstacles that continually popped up for me were also in other people's way, and they are probably in yours, too.

Key learning: Record details of your daily life in business. Not only will it give you invaluable promotional material, it will also declutter your brain.

The Thoughts

This is the central theme to the quite brilliant LinkedIn article by personal branding expert Carlii Lyon, 'Beware of these 3 thoughts on the path to putting yourself out there'.[16] For me, this article sums up perfectly the feelings when the writing phase ends and there are no more excuses for not publishing your book, or the reasons you might invent for not speaking at an event or offering to write for your trade press, etc. I would thoroughly recommend reading the article and following Carlii on LinkedIn.

As she explains, it honestly doesn't matter who you are, what you do, how you do it or why you do it, the chances are, on the path to putting yourself out there and building your profile, you will face one, two or all of these thoughts.

⟡ **Who am I to speak?**
My response: why not? As a reformed pessimist, I can tell you that a zero-negativity mindset will swiftly banish this thought. You are unique. You have something to say. No human is your superior, no human is your inferior. Why the fuck shouldn't you write a book, speak at an event, submit an article, etc?

⟡ **I am not saying anything new, why would anyone care?**
We *greenhouse* ideas at The Point.1888. In other words, we have sessions where none of us can criticise another team member's idea, we can only build on the original

16   C Lyon, 'Beware of these 3 thoughts on the path to putting yourself out there', LinkedIn, 2019, www.linkedin.com/pulse/beware-3-thoughts-path-putting-yourself-out-carlii-lyon

idea. When a team of people plays with a whole bunch of kaleidoscopes, the ideas amplify way beyond what we thought possible.

'Original' thought is rarely original. It is a learning I will take to the grave.

✧ **Everyone will think I have a big ego.**
I struggled with this one the most. Putting yourself out there, opening yourself up, being vulnerable and becoming the person you are destined to be is terrifying. There is no easy way round this one. I hated the thought. But in the end, I just said to myself, 'Fuck it. I don't give a fuck what most people think of me anymore.'

> Key learning: Get out there, be the person you are destined to be. Don't pause for a second to doubt yourself.

You can achieve everything you've ever wanted to. Chase both success and significance equally, even if it takes twenty years to do so. An overnight success is a fallacy. Nothing happens overnight, it's always built on the back of resilience and good, old-fashioned hard work.

But your success story has started happening. Here you are at the end of the first part of your journey.

Surviving your first year in business

This is an incredible achievement – 80% of those who started their adventure when you did have already given up. This is a wakeup call moment.

By the end of Year One, you'll know how hard it is to make money and get paid. You'll know that your dream of more time, more money and less stress is actually a nightmare. But you *will* have built resilience. You'll have learned how to survive. You're also likely to have watched a lot of daytime TV, if your first year goes anything like mine.

Just Survive Somehow. This is your motto. Your mantra. It is the best-case scenario you can wish for, so don't underestimate it. You *can* build your own new life, your own new empire. Piece by piece. Step by step. Inch by inch. By surviving Year One, you are on the journey and dreaming ahead to Year Two and beyond.

Successful businessman and author Daniel Priestley says that starting a business is like a career in boxing.[17] Every victory only leads to a bigger and harder opponent. Are you ready for Year Two? It gets much tougher, mainly because your responsibilities will be much more complex, but with one year under your belt, it's likely you're already a running-your-own-business addict. And after surviving Year One, you will be much tougher than you were.

Many starter-uppers dream of reaching a £1m turnover by Year Three. But the odds are stacked against you. On this journey,

---

17   D Priestley, *Entrepreneur Revolution: How to develop your entrepre-neurial mindset and start a business that works* (Capstone, 2013)

you won't even remember what your comfort zone was. You will touch the void on multiple occasions. It is only you who can ultimately define whether you will be a success, which is lonely. Terrifying. Horrific at times. I know. I assure you, I know. I have been to dark places you probably do not even know exist yet.

> Key learning: Never, **ever** give up.

I interviewed someone recently who had to close a business. I hope I never have to do that; I've heard that it's like a chunk of your life dying. All that effort for nothing. The pain of shutting up shop, closing the door on something you dreamed would change your life. For me, it would be too much to bear. I have huge respect for those who achieve their dream the second or third time round.

Abraham Lincoln failed consistently, from losing his job in 1832 to being defeated for senate for the second time in 1858, but eventually he ended up being elected president in 1860. He never gave up, and became the most powerful human on the planet. You should follow his example.

Legacy

I have just taken a month out of my business to finish this book. I know that I could die tomorrow and my business would live on (not that I have any intention of dying anytime soon). My incredible team now runs my business. I am needed for leadership, coaching and opinions, but that is all. That is the dream scenario for those who value time over money.

This is an incredibly comforting position to have reached. My legacy will live on. When you get to this point yourself, you will know how special a realisation it is. It only took me five years to get here. You can do it too.

The true meaning of life

A friend of mine suffered a completely unexpected aneurysm (weakening of an artery wall) on Christmas Day in 2011. He was twenty-eight. He spent months in a coma and has since learned to recover some movement in his body, but his life has been turned upside down.

My friend's body was damaged, but his mind and sense of humour have been untouched. We discussed some pretty heavy topics during his recovery, one of which was the meaning of life. When you have lost as much as he has, it's certainly something you contemplate a lot.

My friend's circumstances serve as a reminder of how fragile life is. Now, I have my own 'Meaning of Life':

- ❖ Do something you love
- ❖ Find someone to love
- ❖ Help others through nothing but love

> Key learning: Love **IS** the answer.

Freedom and choice can soon be yours. You have one opportunity. One small window of time on this planet. If you don't do it, you *will* regret it.

Time is more valuable than money. Make this central in your startup thinking. The sooner you accept that as core to your life, the sooner you will be happy and no longer crave pointless things.

> Key learning: We can sometimes feel we have all the time in the world. We don't. Choose what to do with every second wisely.

Good luck. Preparing for and surviving Year One is a big step on your journey through life, so I hope this book has helped in some small way. Can you imagine where you could be one year from now? Really visualise what you and your startup could become: limitless and free.

If you've read this far – thank you. This is the end, for now. It's your turn. By the end of Year One, if you're not bankrupt, dead or in prison, give yourself a high-five. You are a startup winner.

You have one simple task: *Just Survive Somehow*. And if you are in need of a stranger's hand in a desperate land, please contact me at justsurvivesomehow@thepoint1888.com

CHEAT SHEET

You've done it! You've survived Year One! Let's have a quick look back over this final chapter in your *Just Survive Somehow* journey.

✧ Shout it from the rooftops – or from LinkedIn, or YouTube, or networking events: you're in business.

✧ Make copious notes each day to make sure you have plenty to tell people when you're networking and prospecting.

✧ Work out what is important to you in life and go for it.

✧ The future –picture what it could be. Never stop dreaming of what you could achieve.

✧ Never, ever give up – it's how you will survive.

BIBLIOGRAPHY

I have only added a short reading list because, hey, we are all busy! Much of your learning can come from articles on LinkedIn and videos on YouTube as this is an easier way of digesting content quickly, but there is something special about the storytelling feeling of the books on my list. These stories will help you dream, and you will need to dream.

It is important you find the books and authors that resonate with you. These are the ones that allowed me to realise my dream. I have added them in the order I would read them if I was starting from scratch.

Byrne, R, *The Secret* (Simon & Schuster, 2006)

Reed, R, Balon, A, Wright, J, *A Book About Innocent: Our story and some things we've learned* (Michael Joseph, 2009)

Branson, R, *Losing My Virginity: The autobiography* (Virgin Digital, 2011)

Watt, J, *Business for Punks: Break all the rules – the BrewDog way* (Penguin, 2016)

Conniff, S, Barker, A, *How to Be More Pirate* (Penguin, 2018)

Priestley, D, *Entrepreneur Revolution: How to develop your entrepreneurial mindset and start a business that works* (Capstone, 2013)

Levitt, SD, Dubner, SJ, *Freakonomics: A rogue economist explores the hidden side of everything* (Penguin, 2007)

Klein, N, *No Logo* (Random House, 1999)

Sinek, S, *Start With Why: How great leaders inspire everyone to take action* (Penguin, 2011)

Priestley, D, *Key Person of Influence: The five-step method to become one of the most highly valued and highly paid people in your industry* (Rethink Press, 2014)

ACKNOWLEDGEMENTS

There are certainly a few diamonds who have helped me over my mental hurdles during the writing process. Thank you to:

Geraldine Brennan and Kate Latham for truly understanding me and the message I wanted to give to the world.

Lucy McCarraher for being honest with the first draft and holding me to account.

Zoe Stewart for always having my back, believing in me and giving my dream purpose.

Carlii Lyon for educating me on The Thoughts and helping me overcome them.

Huge Stewart for the drive, resilience and pride.

Lisa Hopkinson for inspiring me to be different, stubborn and honest in all aspects of business.

Martin McLaughlin for listening to the live audio version of the now defunct Chapter 10 and giving me my mojo back when I fell at the last hurdle.

To the best human team in history at The Point.1888 for running my business while I pursued this project.

And finally, to everyone who believed in me when I first started talking about starting my own business. I promise I won't let you down.

Or should I do as Spike Milligan once said: 'I'm not going to thank anybody because I did it all on my own'? After a rollercoaster thirty-month writing journey, part of me relates to Spike. This book has most certainly tested my personal drive and resilience.

THE AUTHOR

Will Stewart is founder and CEO of The Point.1888, the UK's fastest growing brand licensing agency. He studied Marketing and International Business before completing a Post graduate Diploma in Retail.

Will is a retail, brand and product expert with over twenty years' experience in a variety of sectors and channels. His retail knowledge was developed during his time at Kingfisher plc, Woolworths, Sainsbury's and the John Lewis Partnership, before changing industry, company and role to join The Licensing Company to work with some of the biggest brands on the planet.

Will launched The Point.1888 in 2015, a business using its purpose and values to disrupt a 150-year-old growing industry through new methodology and innovation, leading to Will winning the licensing industry's Brand Ambassador Award in 2020 five years after the company was established. The business has won numerous awards, including the Tesco Values Award in 2017, and Will received the Institute of Directors Start Up Director of the Year Award in 2018. The Point.1888 has established its reputation through donating eleven percent of its profits to charity and secured outstanding talent through its market-leading ultra-flexibility policies, focussing on true life-work balance for its team.

Will is passionate about business being a force for good, through humans starting and growing purpose-driven businesses and using purpose as a central mission to disrupt big industries. To support this, his second company, True Purpose Enterprises Ltd, has been created to empower and support purpose-driven businesses to punch above their weight.

Contact Will at:

- www.willstewart1888.com
- https://thepoint1888.com
- www.linkedin.com/in/willstewart1888